Folens

GCSE PE

For EDEXCEL
TEACHER'S GUIDE

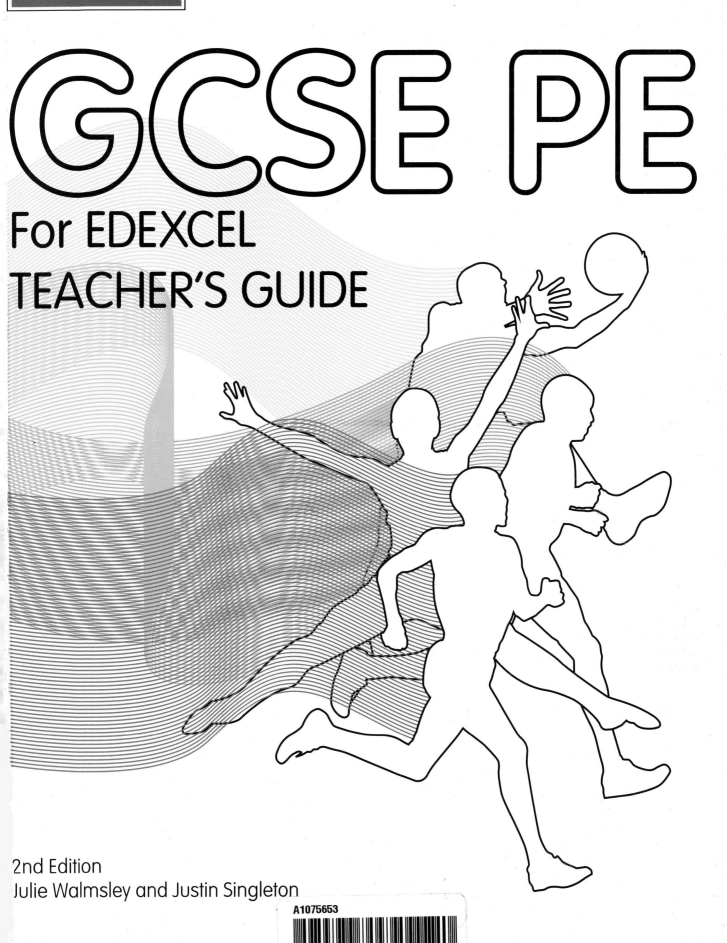

2nd Edition

Julie Walmsley and Justin Singleton

Acknowledgements

p.14 © PA/Empics; p.15 © PA/Empics; p.16 © Action Plus; p.17 © Action Plus; p.18 (top, bottom) © PA/Empics; p.18 (middle) © Action Plus; p.32 © Action Plus; p.64 © iStockphoto.com/Lighthousebay; p.65 © iStockphoto.com/Lighthousebay; p.72 © PA/Empics; p.73 © PA/Empics; p.88 © PA/Empics; p.97 © Action Plus; p.98 © Action Plus; p.101 © PA/Empics; p.102 © PA/Empics; p.107 © PA/Empics; p.142 © iStockphoto.com/Sportstock; p.154 (top, middle, bottom) © PA/Empics; p.155 (top, middle, bottom) © PA/Empics; p.175 © Action Plus; p.176 © Action Plus; p.179 (top) © Action Plus; p.179 (top middle, bottom middle, bottom) © PA/Empics; p.180 (top) © Action Plus; p.180 (top middle, bottom middle, bottom) © PA/Empics; p.185 © PA/Empics; p.191 © Action Plus; p.192 © Action Plus; p.193 © Action Plus; p.194 © Action Plus; p.197 © PA/Empics; p.199 © PA/Empics; p.200 © PA/Empics; p.201 © PA/Empics;

© 2009 Folens Limited, on behalf of the author.

United Kingdom: Folens Publishers, Waterslade House, Thame Road, Haddenham,
Buckinghamshire HP17 8NT.
Email: folens@folens.com   Website: www.folens.com

Ireland: Folens Publishers, Greenhills Road, Tallaght, Dublin 24.
Email: info@folens.ie   Website: www.folens.ie

Editor: Rosie Parrish
Text design: Form
Layout: Planman
Picture researcher: Thelma Gilbert
Illustrations: Planman
Cover design: Design by Form (www.form.uk.com)

For general spellings Folens adheres to *Oxford Dictionary of English,* Second Edition (Revised), 2005.

First published 2009 by Folens Limited.

ISBN 978-1-85008-400-6
Folens code FD4006

Contents

Introduction

The Teacher's Guide

Using this Teacher's Guide

The GCSE PE for Edexcel Student's Book and the GCSE PE for Edexcel Teacher's Guide together represent detailed coverage of the content of the Edexcel specification, and both follow the order of the specification. By setting out the content in this way, it becomes easier for you to monitor students' progress through the specification and each section can be checked off when planning revision.

By working through the Student's Book alongside the Teacher's Guide, using the Worksheets, Homework sheets, Extension sheets and PowerPoint® slides, students should have an excellent opportunity to follow the specification and complete a variety of work on each of the topics. As a result they will have the opportunity to continually learn and revisit core information, and so have a good chance of remembering it for the examination. All the work in the Student's Book and the Teacher's Guide presents information at an appropriate GCSE level, and should equip students with all the necessary knowledge and skills to deal with the final examination.

Many of the questions posed in the Worksheets, Homework sheets, Extension sheets and PowerPoint® slides are along the lines of those students will come across in the final exam. This should allow them to build familiarity with answering questions on subjects they will need to know about, and they will become more confident in dealing with them.

The contents of the Teacher's Guide extends the learning covered in the Student's Book. For each section of the Student's Book the Guide contains a series of Worksheets, Homework sheets, Extension sheets and PowerPoint® slides. The sequence and order of topics in the Teacher's Guide relates to the order of topics in the Student's Book, making it straightforward for you to manage and administer.

As each school using these materials will have their own lesson length and timetabling in which to deliver the course, there are no prescriptive lesson plans provided in the Teacher's Guide. You therefore have the freedom and flexibility to use your own method of setting out the content of the lesson in the time available. This is important, as some students in the class may need a more flexible approach to receive the full benefit of the lesson content.

Good practice in PE lessons suggests that a lesson tends to involve some or all of the following:
- registering students and collecting and recording homework
- stating the learning objectives of the lesson
- an introduction to the work for the day
- whole-class work on the topic; for example, reading from the Student's Book, reading newspaper cuttings, watching a video or a PowerPoint® presentation, and so on
- a whole-class discussion
- individual/pairs/small group student work on a specific topic
- round up of the work studied with the whole group
- the setting of homework/revision.

The structure of the Teacher's Guide

By working through the Teacher's Guide and the Student's Book, the whole theory section of the Edexcel specification (Unit 1) will be covered. Using the material in the Teacher's Guide reinforces the development of knowledge and skills in the Student's Book by providing tasks relevant to each topic. The Teacher's Guide and the Student's Book work together to give the maximum opportunity for students to read, learn and understand each topic.

The support materials in this Guide take the form of:
- differentiated Worksheets (Level A and Level B) related to the Student's Book topics
- Homework sheets
- Extension sheets providing extra work
- PowerPoint® slides providing topic summaries, extra information and tasks

The Worksheets, Homework sheets and Extension sheets are also available in Word format on the CD-ROM so you can edit them to suit the needs of your students.

There are a variety of tasks and activities used across all the support material in this Guide, which include:
• use of word and statement banks to complete sentences and paragraphs
• finishing partly completed diagrams
• diagrams with the initials of the correct label next to the part
• linking exercises: joining two parts of a sentence or statement together
• correct ordering of text
• grouping relevant information together
• use of observation skills to answer questions
• completing tables with information from the Student's Book or from word banks.

Worksheets

When working through the Student's Book there may be times when some students find the task on the page too difficult to complete. For the majority of tasks in the Student's Book there is an accompanying Worksheet in the Teacher's Guide for students who need extra help or a more structured way of completing the task and learning the material. This allows the inclusion of all students in the learning process.

Two versions of all the worksheets are provided. Level A worksheets are for the more-able student as they are more demanding. Level B worksheets offer more help and support for less-able students. The graded worksheets will always lead to an examination-level answer, which will earn marks in the final exam. The difference between the tasks in the Student's Book and the separate worksheets is that the graded tasks allow the student to reach the appropriate answers in a more structured manner. This allows all students to succeed, have the right information in front of them and have worthy revision material for a later date.

Homework sheets

Each section in the Teacher's Guide includes Homework sheets to reinforce the topic studied. These can be used to ask students to use different skills to complete tasks, in order to maximize effective methods of learning. For example, students can be asked to:
• find a new way to answer a question covered in the lesson
• learn some information from the lesson
• answer a task that acts as revision, adapting the information learnt in class to answer new questions
• interpret information or statistics given in graphs or diagrams
• work independently using information on the Homework sheet
• complete an exam-type question.

Extension sheets

Extension sheets provide extra work on some topics. They are designed to provide additional challenges for students who quickly grasp and understand the information. Often, extension work will provide a greater challenge for students and demand a longer answer from them.

PowerPoint® slides

The PowerPoint® slides provide a summary of each of the topics covered in the Student's Book. They have been designed as a starting point for teachers to work from in lessons and can be adapted to suit individual needs. Tasks have also been provided as a starting point for lesson activities for different learning abilities. Exam questions have been provided so that knowledge from the slides can be applied.

Answer section

Where appropriate, answers for the tasks in the Student's Book, Worksheets, Homework sheets and Extension sheets are provided at the back of the Teacher's Guide in the Answer section. It is hoped that provision of these will lessen the burden of marking and can also be used by the students to mark their own work, check their corrections and as a revision source. For those tasks or questions with no set answer, students' work should be marked on its own merits.

Practical application of the Student's Book and Teacher's Guide

To use the Student's Book and the Teacher's Guide together and get the best use of both, there needs to be an element of preparation by you prior to lessons. This is often based on the knowledge of the class itself or the previous recorded results of the class. Each Worksheet has the section, topic, Student's Book page reference and level of sheet clearly marked on the sheet. This makes it easy to manage when linking worksheets with the Student's Book tasks. This will hopefully make the organization and grouping together of worksheets for the appropriate topics easier.

As the Student's Book and Teacher's Guide work through the specification, work can be prepared in blocks, or section by section, or on an individual lesson basis. Each approach has its own advantages and disadvantages:

In blocks

- Preparation is completed for longer periods of time, allowing you to concentrate on other administrative matters.
- This will need a lot of time and effort to complete each block.
- Storage for all work needs to be in place.

Section by section

- Duplicating all the information for one section may take some time, so perhaps this can be done once every term.
- The teacher delivering the information could have the photocopied sheets for the whole topic in a ring binder and each levelled task in a plastic sleeve.
- All the information will be at hand, so if a student has finished a piece of work, an Extension sheet from the Teacher's Guide can be used. In this way a student can reinforce work covered and use time effectively.
- When the section is coming to an end, sheets not used can be used to practise and revise for the test.
- As each section is finished, the information can simply be put back into storage.
- At the start of the second delivery of the course (the next year 10 group) there will already be a complete set of resources for use in the department.

Individual lessons

- Preparation takes less time but has to be done more often.
- Gives the opportunity to look over the work again and refresh the topic information.
- Gives scope to vary the number of photocopies according to students' needs.

Optimizing students' performance

You may wish to consider the following list of methods for optimizing students' performance, which is based on the authors' experience of teaching PE at GCSE level:
- Informing students of what they need to know in order to succeed can improve results.
- Give students their own photocopy of the specification to keep in their workbook or file, or providing an abbreviated version to help them to prepare for and focus on the topics.
- Students to set their own targets on their test results.
- Regular testing will help show students' understanding of the topic covered.
- Going through tests to correct and add in information is important.
- Completed tests can be placed in students' workbooks or files and used as a revision aid.

Key skills

GCSE PE Unit 1 can fulfil some of the key skills set out by the Qualification and Curriculum Authority (QCA). These include:
- Communication Level 2 C2.1a
- Communication Level 2 C2.2
- ICT2.1: Find and select information

The particular communication skills are recognized as those needed in everyday life, work, education and training.

Throughout this Teacher's Guide there are opportunities for discussion, researching different forms of information and using ICT skills.

C2.1a

Take part in a group discussion:

2.1a.1 Make clear and relevant contributions in a way that suits your purpose and situation
2.1a.2 Respond appropriately to others
2.1a.3 Help to move the discussion forward

The following are some possible areas where these criteria can come about:
- Active challenge discussions with a partner or in a group
- Answering questions appropriately
- Listening to others and their opinions when sharing information
- Asking questions on a given topic in discussions to further ideas.

C2.2

Read and summarize information from at least two documents about the same subject. Each document must be a minimum of 500 words long:

2.2.1 Select and read relevant documents
2.2.2 Identify accurately the main points, ideas and lines of reasoning
2.2.3 Summarize the information to suit your purpose

The following are some possible areas where these criteria can come about:
- Obtaining information from reading articles, reports and textbooks on given topics
- Skimming documents to make sure they are relevant
- Scanning documents and picking out the main points
- Collecting information from different sources
- Summarizing information in tables, spider diagrams, lists, and so on.

ICT2.1

Search for and select information:

2.1.1   Select information relevant to the tasks:
- search and select information to meet your needs
- use different information sources for each task and multiple search criteria in at least one case
- identify suitable sources of information from ICT sources and non-ICT sources (for example, written documents, files, CD-ROMs)
- search for information using multiple search criteria (such as using AND or '<' '>' or '+' and '–' in search engines)
- interpret information (for example, respond to an enquiry, write a project report).

Some possible areas where these criteria can come about:
- Identifying suitable sources for information including documents, files, CD-ROMs
- Searching different sources for information
- Building up a search on a subject using written documents, files, CD-ROMs and search engines.
- Interpreting information by writing a report and responding to a question.

Teaching ideas

To help students revise and for information to stick in their minds more easily, it is a good idea to adopt a range of teaching ideas such as the ones in this section. They also help to present information in a more fun, accessible and interactive way.

Revision

- Students could list all of the topics covered in the GCSE PE course so they can tick them off as they revise them.
- Students could be encouraged to create a revision timetable, covering all of the topics they need to revise. Revision time should be broken up evenly between each topic with plenty of regular breaks (a ten minute break every hour will help students to keep their concentration). Students should work out which topics they find harder than others and set aside more time to cover them in their timetable.

Revision skills

- Students could create revision cards on each topic by writing key points, phrases, diagrams and words and then connect them together.
- Students could produce audio notes using a Dictaphone to play back at any time.
- Students could place stick-it notes around their room or home with key points or phrases written on them so they are reminded frequently. Family and friends could also be encouraged to ask random questions relating to each topic.
- Students could pair up as 'revision buddies' to help bounce ideas off each other, help with testing knowledge and to make revision more fun.

Mastermind quiz

This idea can be adapted to most subjects.

Each student declares their specialist subject.

During class or for homework each student revises their subject and compiles 12 questions and answers on it.

Students submit their questions and answers to the teacher prior to the lesson who will then randomly create small groups of students and allocate a set of questions to each student.

In the designated lesson, each student will face 12 questions on someone else's specialist subject within their group.

The roles in the group can be shared so that everyone is involved:
- quiz master (students take it in turns to ask the others questions)
- scorer (students take it in turns to keep score)
- pass recorder (students take it in turns to keep track of the number of passes).

Students are to feedback on their groups results.

You can evaluate what students already know and the areas that need to be revisited.

Sports reporting

This idea can be adapted to most subjects, such as:
- reviewing a training programme
- reaction to a game
- comments on different systems before, during and after exercise
- recommended diet for a particular event.

Students are to act as both a sports reporter and a sportsperson.

Each student is randomly allocated a subject, which they will need to create five questions for.

In pairs, students take it in turns to act as a sports reporter interviewing a sportsperson. Each interview should last for three minutes.

Students should then write up their interview as a sports report.

Feedback should be given by students as to what they now know as a result of the interview. They should also state if they feel they asked good questions or what they would ask next time.

Cards with linking ideas: deal, pick up and make sets

This idea is adaptable for many subjects, such as circulatory, respiratory, muscular and skeletal systems, training methods, training principles, and so on.

Choose five to seven subjects. (This will depend on the number of students in the class.)

For each subject, write down a word or phrase on five cards (one word/phrase per card) that relates to that subject. These can be colour-coded for lower-ability students.

The cards are shuffled and dealt to the whole class. Each student is dealt five cards each. The remaining cards are the 'pick up pile'.

The student to the left of the dealer starts by picking up a card from the pick up pile. They need to check it against the cards in their hand and then place any unwanted card back onto the pick up pile.

The object of the game is for students to collect all of the five cards relevant to a subject and name the subject.

The first student to declare a five-card set is the winner.

The game can either stop or carry on, finding a student for second place.

Information posters

This idea can be adapted to most subjects.

Students are to create an information poster to include all of the main points and facts in relation to a specified subject.

The poster must have visual impact and be informative to others.

The posters could include:
- facts and information students have researched themselves
- technical diagrams
- photos and images that students have researched and collected themselves.

The answers quiz

This idea can be adapted to most subjects.

Each student must come up with a word or sentence as an answer. This is written on the whiteboard.

Another student then has to come up with a question to go with the answer.

This idea would also work if students were to write a number of answers on a sheet of paper and swap their sheet with a partner. Each student would need to come up with questions to go with each answer.

Working in pairs

This idea is for learning the bones of the skeleton and the names of the muscles.

In pairs, one student writes down the name of a main bone or muscle on a stick-it note and then sticks it on their partner to show where that bone is located. Students take it in turns to write and stick.

Working in pairs or threes

This idea is for learning the bones, joints and muscles.

In pairs or groups of three, students take it in turns to draw a bone shape on the playground in chalk, label it and explain the image to another group.

Infomercial

This idea can be adapted to most subjects but is specifically appropriate to work on drugs, media and technology.

In pairs or groups of four, students use media to create an infomercial on anything sports-related. This could include:
- an MP3 recorder for a 30 second radio-style advert
- a video camera for a one minute television advert.

You should give a specific timeframe for students to prepare their infomercials. You should then set them a specific time for them to film or record their infomercial.

The adverts should be played to the class with feedback given by the group that created it and the rest of the class.

Sport challenge

This idea can be adapted to most subjects.

You are to set questions on one particular subject or a range of subjects.

Students are divided into four teams (depending on the size of the class).

Ask each team in turn a question. For each question the team gets right they score a point. For each question they get wrong they lose a point. If the team passes on a question, they lose a point and any other team can answer the question for a bonus point.

Snowballing

This idea can be adapted to most subjects.

For example, each student has to think of three ways to exercise. They then talk to someone else in the class and exchange their ideas.

A time limit could be imposed in which students have to collect as many ideas from others as possible, or students can stop once they have ten additional ideas, different to the three they thought of.

Songs for learning

This idea can be adapted to any subject.

Choose a well-known song such as Queen's *We Will Rock You*.

You can either choose a subject and write words to the chosen tune on that subject or chose a subject and ask students in pairs or groups to come up with the words to the tune.

The lyric sheets can then be copied and distributed so that the whole class can sing along.

The music will act as an accompaniment; if using the Queen song, everyone can do the drumbeat using their hands on their desks.

Yes/no questions

This idea can be adapted to any subject.

Each student is given a term on a stick-it note which they are not allowed to read.

Students put the stick-it note on their head and go around the room asking everyone one question about the term they have. Students are only allowed to ask questions that will elicit a yes or no answer.

This idea really encourages students to think about topics by limiting them to only yes and no answers.

Blockbusters

This idea can be adapted to any subject.

Write letters in interconnecting hexagons on the board.

In turn, students pick a letter from the board and answer a question related to that letter. For example, 'What F is a health-related exercise component?'.

Millionaire

This idea can be adapted to any subject.

A range of easy to hard questions are created on all subjects, either by you or the students, with four answer options for each question.

Students can take it in turns to be the quiz host asking the questions and the contestant.

The quiz host can be changed after every correct answer given to allow all students to get involved.

The student contestant stays on for as long as they answer the questions correctly.

Hangman

This idea can be adapted to any subject.

Students can work in pairs or a small group versus another small group.

In their pairs, or small groups, a student writes lines on the board indicating a word or words relating to a particular subject.

The other person in the pair, or others in the group, have to guess the correct letters that make up the word.

If the letter they guess is correct, it gets written on the board. If it is incorrect, the letter gets written on the board and crossed out. One part of the hangman is then drawn.

The game continues until all letters have been guessed correctly or the hangman has been drawn completely.

A question of sport

This idea can be adapted to any subject.

There are a variety of ways to conduct this task, including:

- The picture round: students are to get into teams. A theme such as 'food' is chosen by one team and examples are collected using the Internet. The pictures are then shown to the other team who have to identify what the picture is (for example, bread – carbohydrate).
- On the buzzer: quick fire questions are given on a specific subject; the first team or student to put their hand up has a chance to answer the question and score a point.
- Home or away: students work in teams. One member of the team nominates a subject for the other team to ask and chooses to either answer a 'home' question for one point or an 'away' question for two points (the 'away' question will be slightly harder).
- What happens next?: a video clip is shown or an action is described (for example, a sporting action or body action such as the circulation of blood) but with the final stage of the action left out. Students then have to explain what happens next.
- Charades: a nominated member of a team sees a picture or word given to them by the opposite team and acts it out for their own team to guess.

Big scale understanding

This idea can be adapted to the circulatory, respiratory and muscular systems.

This is a whole class activity and should take place in the playground.

Chalk a simple diagram of the heart on the playground.

Students should be split into two teams – the red team and the blue team – and wear appropriate coloured bibs.

The red team indicates oxygenated blood and the blue team indicates deoxygenated blood.

In their teams, students should organize themselves around the heart diagram to show the flow of blood according to their coloured bib.

This idea has a high impact on students and really encourages them to think.

Create your own links

This idea can be adapted to any subject.

Provide pairs or small groups of students with a set of four small cards and a specific subject each – making sure they keep the subject secret from other groups.

Each pair or group writes down four words (one per card) that link to the subject they have been given. For example, they are given the subject of 'joints' so they could write down a type of joint, a name of a joint, a movement of a joint and a sporting example. The cards should be checked to make sure the links are correct.

All of the finished cards then get mixed up together.

Once mixed together, all of the other cards are turned over so students can see what is written on them.

Each group is then given a card with a specific subject on it – this is the subject they need to find the correct four linking cards for. This card should be kept secret from the other groups with each group taking it in turns to choose a card from the file. If they decide they have chosen an incorrect card they have to put it back in the file on their next go, without choosing a replacement card.

This activity can be timed for the more competitive students.

There can be any number of links, but sets of four are a good working number.

Practical application

This idea uses circuit training, is a whole class activity and uses overload.

Either set up a general fitness circuit or ask students to create a circuit in groups. There are three levels of work: either 30 seconds, 45 seconds or one minute.

Students should choose the option that will challenge them.

Thought processing

This idea can be adapted to any subject. It is a whole class activity.

You will need:
- a chair
- a waste-paper bin
- a ball of paper
- a ground floor classroom with an opened window.

A model should be created for a simple task to be demonstrated by a volunteer. For example: a student sits on a chair and throws the ball of paper out of the window, aiming for the waste-paper bin outside.

Go through each stage of this model with the class and ask them what they have to think about at each step.

Once students have worked through the premise of a model, this can be moved into the sports hall and adapted to real game situations.

Dance and types of movement

Students, working as individuals, pairs or groups should create a dance routine using different types of movement such as abduction, adduction and so on.

1.1 Healthy, active lifestyles

1.1.1 Healthy, active lifestyles and how they could benefit you

Contents

Worksheets

Homework sheet

Extension sheets

13

Worksheet 1: Positive effects of exercise

Level A   Student's Book pages 10–19

Task

Study the headings below and then compose two sentences that give examples for each heading. One sentence has been done for you as an example.

Physical effects

1 — More energy

I have been training for several sessions and I seem to be able to keep working for longer without tiring, despite the fact that my training sessions are getting harder.

2 — Increase in fitness

3 — Participation will increase life expectancy

4 — Meeting challenges

Mental effects

5 — Feeling good

6 — Can appreciate the finer points of the activity

7 — Learning new skills

8 — Excitement through the activity

Worksheet 1: Positive effects of exercise

Level B **Student's Book pages 10–19**

Task

The subheadings below, numbered one to eight, are divided into physical effects and mental effects. Link the statements, labelled a to p, to the correct subheading by writing the letter of the relevant statement in the box next to the subheading. There are two statements for every heading.

Physical effects

1 — More energy

2 — Increase in fitness

3 — Participation will increase life expectancy

4 — Meeting challenges

Mental effects

5 — Feeling good

6 — Can appreciate the finer points of the activity

7 — Learning new skills

8 — Excitement through the activity

a) "Having played the game I can see how hard top-class sportspeople work."

b) "My pulse rate per minute is reducing. This means my heart does not have to work so hard."

c) "The rush of skiing at my maximum speed downhill is what I really enjoy."

d) "I have been training for several sessions and I seem to be able to keep working for longer without tiring, despite the fact that my training sessions are getting harder."

e) "I enjoy starting a new sport, learning and using the new skills involved."

f) "Through exercising regularly I have lost weight. This makes me positive about myself."

g) "I am becoming more confident about my ability to meet the challenges of the sport and realize how important it is to keep to my training plan."

h) "I exercise for general fitness so I can keep my heart and lungs in good working order for longer."

i) "The more exercise I do, the more energy I seem to have."

j) "Canoeing white-water rapids takes my skills to the edge; it's the reason I enjoy the sport so much!"

k) "When I started the sport I knew little about the tactics, but now I find great enjoyment in outwitting the opposition due to what I have learnt."

l) "After reaching a set goal in a training session I feel better both physically and mentally."

m) "I am confident in the knowledge that my individual training plan increases the strength and durability of my heart and lungs."

n) "As a result of training regularly I am stronger and can keep working for longer without tiring."

o) "My training and improved skills give me the confidence to meet the physical challenges of the game."

p) "When I watch a game on television I understand how skilful the players are, due to my own experiences of the game."

Homework 1: Why do people take part in sport?

Student's Book pages 10–19

Task

Match the statements labelled a to i to the three types of people listed below. Write the letter and the statement in the spaces provided.

a) "I enjoy training on my own."

b) "Each year we go on tour to a different country."

c) "After the game the social life is brilliant."

d) "It is an interesting process having to work out my training schedule according to when the competitions take place."

e) "I have improved my body shape since starting my training programme."

f) "My favourite part of taking part is the final competition."

g) "I vary the types of exercise I do in my training programme."

h) "I enjoy the physical nature of the sport."

i) "I can choose to work on my own or with others."

1 — Rugby player

_____

_____

_____

_____

2 — Middle-distance runner

_____

_____

_____

_____

3 — Leisure club member

_____

_____

_____

_____

Extension 1: Positive benefits of physical activity

Student's Book pages 10–19

Tasks

1 — Study the information below, which outlines the positive benefits of physical activity.

2 — Connect each of the middle sections to the appropriate side boxes. One has been done for you as an example.

Can help relieve stress and tension

Provides enjoyment

Encourages social mixing

Improves team and cooperation skills

Provides a physical challenge

Helps physical development

Helps a person to look and feel good

Provides opportunity for competition

Helps mental development

Can provide stimulation and excitement

Gain membership to a particular sports club

Helps social development

Contributes to good health

Allows a person to take part in a sport

Encourages friendship

Gives opportunities for aesthetic appreciation

Helps to improve body shape

Extension 2: Different reasons for choosing physical activity

Student's Book pages 10–19

Task

Study the photos below and decide why each of the people shown have chosen to take part in that particular activity.

There are ideas in the box below to help you.

List the reasons why in the space provided.

Possible reasons

- For enjoyment
- To gain membership of a sports club
- Activity is stimulating
- Contributes to good health
- Encourages friendship
- Meet others with similar interests

- To help look and feel good
- Relieve tension and stress
- Provides physical challenges
- Provides competition
- Gives a chance to take part in an activity
- Improves body shape

1.1.1 Healthy, active lifestyles and how they could benefit you

© Folens (copiable page)

Extension 3: A survey on reasons for participation in physical activity

Student's Book pages 10–19

Tasks

1 — Ask ten people why they participate in physical activity. Have them provide between five and ten different reasons.

2 — Divide the responses into physical, mental and social reasons and create a bar chart in the space below to show how common each response is.

3 — Create a report in your workbook, bringing together the variety of reasons everyone provided.

You could also ask them how competitive they are and whether that makes a difference to why they participate in sport.

1.1 Healthy, active lifestyles

1.1.2 Influences on your healthy, active lifestyle

Contents

Worksheets

Homework sheets

Extension sheets

Worksheet 1: Parents, teachers and peers

Level A   **Student's Book pages 37–39**

Tasks

1 — Read the comments below which encourage a young person to participate in sport. Each may have been said by a parent, a teacher or a peer.

Decide who would have said each comment and write them under each heading below. Each heading has three comments linked with it.

2 — Now add two more comments for each heading, which add to the list of encouragements.

Comments

"You'll be the only one that does not play!"

"I can show you how to live a healthy life."

"You will have the opportunity to take part in sport at different levels."

"What are you scared of?"

"I can see ability in you, so try this sport."

"I played for the local team just like my father."

"We lacked confidence at the beginning, but once we got to know people it was fine."

"We will give you the chance to experience the use of local facilities."

"Come with us – you'll really enjoy it!"

Parent

_____

_____

_____

_____

Teacher

_____

_____

_____

_____

_____

Peer

_____

_____

_____

_____

Worksheet 1: Parents, teachers and peers

Level B   **Student's Book pages 37–39**

Task

Read the comments below which encourage a young person to participate in sport. Each may have been said by a parent, a teacher or a peer.

Decide who would have said each comment and write them under each heading below. Each heading has three comments linked with it.

Comments

"You'll be the only one that does not play!"

"I can show you how to live a healthy life."

"You will have the opportunity to take part in sport at different levels."

"What are you scared of?"

"I can see ability in you, so try this sport."

"I played for the local team just like my father."

"We lacked confidence at the beginning, but once we got to know people it was fine."

"We will give you the chance to experience the use of local facilities."

"Come with us – you'll really enjoy it!"

Parent

_____

_____

_____

Teacher

_____

_____

_____

Peer

_____

_____

_____

1.1.2 Influences on your healthy, active lifestyle   © Folens (copiable page)

Worksheet 2: Social reasons affecting participation

Level A **Student's Book pages 39–42**

Tasks

1 — Read the three comments below which have been made by keen and talented sportspeople. Study their problems and think of possible ways they could overcome them and play the sport of their choice.

> Link your ideas with those from the Student's Book.

Comment A: "I want to play tennis but there are no facilities close by."

Comment B: "Everyone says I am a talented footballer but my family are enthusiastic that I follow family traditions and play rugby."

Comment C: "I can beat children four years older than me but I am told I am too young to join my local team."

2 — Link the suggestions given below to each of the problems above. Write the letter of the problem next to the relevant suggestions.

a) Start a team of your own age ☐

b) Lobby your MP for new facilities ☐

c) Convince others of your seriousness about playing ☐

d) Get sponsorship ☐

e) Prove your skills are comparable to others ☐

f) Travel or move ☐

g) Have other people express their opinion of your skills ☐

h) Practice until eligible ☐

i) Show rewards of the sport ☐

3 — Write three sentences stating the difficulties a disabled person may find when trying to participate in sport.

_____

_____

_____

_____

_____

_____

Worksheet 2: Social reasons affecting participation

Level B   **Student's Book pages 39–42**

Tasks

1 — Read the three comments below which have been made by keen and talented sportspeople. Study their problems and think of possible ways they could overcome them and play the sport of their choice.

> Link your ideas with those from the Student's Book.

Comment A: "I want to play tennis but there are no facilities close by."

Comment B: "Everyone says I am a talented footballer but my family are enthusiastic that I follow family traditions and play rugby."

Comment C: "I can beat children four years older than me but I am told I am too young to join my local team."

2 — Link the suggestions given below to each of the problems above. Write the letter of the problem next to the relevant suggestions.

a) Start a team of your own age   ☐

b) Lobby your MP for new facilities   ☐

c) Convince others of your seriousness about playing   ☐

d) Get sponsorship   ☐

e) Prove your skills are comparable to others   ☐

f) Travel or move   ☐

g) Have other people express their opinion of your skills   ☐

h) Practice until eligible   ☐

i) Show rewards of the sport   ☐

1.1.2 Influences on your healthy, active lifestyle   © Folens (copiable page)

Worksheet 3: Joining a club

Level A   **Student's Book pages 21–42**

Tasks

1— Write out what you would say to a friend to encourage and persuade them to join your sports club. Include four different reasons.

> Include reasons about why people get involved, where it takes place, the kind of activity and how it makes you feel.
>
> You could use some of these key phrases to help start your sentences:
>
> "It's exciting…"
> "Lots of people our age go…"
> "It's very competitive…"
> "My ability has got much better…"

1. _____

_____

2. _____

_____

3. _____

_____

4. _____

_____

2 — Use the following headings to compose your own sentences on the possible positive effects of joining a club.

a) Coaching staff

_____

_____

b) Facilities

_____

_____

c) Social

_____

_____

d) Feel better after a game

_____

_____

e) Club membership privileges

_____

_____

f) Competition

_____

_____

g) Confidence

_____

_____

Worksheet 3: Joining a club

Level B   **Student's Book pages 21–42**

Tasks

1 — Write out what you would say to a friend to encourage and persuade them to join your sports club. Include four different reasons.

> Include reasons about why people get involved, where it takes place, the kind of activity and how it makes you feel.
>
> You could use some of these key phrases to help start your sentences:
>
> "It's exciting…"
> "Lots of people our age go…"
> "It's very competitive…"
> "My ability has got much better…"

1. _____

   _____

2. _____

   _____

3. _____

   _____

4. _____

   _____

2 — Rearrange the words below to make logical sentences which encourage people to take part in sport.

a) best in the county The facilities at our club are the

_____

_____

b) Membership new coach arrived is rising fast, since the

_____

_____

c) after the matches The people at the club we always go out for a drink are so friendly;

_____

_____

d) satisfied and calm after a good workout I feel so relaxed,

_____

_____

e) we can come it means that and play whenever we like By joining the club,

_____

_____

f) I never thought to join in the competitions club I was competitive until I started

_____

_____

g) the people at the club I was shy to begin with, but that I have grown in confidence made me feel so welcome

_____

_____

Worksheet 4: Terrestrial and subscription television

Level A   **Student's Book pages 30–37**

Tasks

1 — Write a paragraph on how terrestrial and subscription television differ. Use some of the key phrases below as a starting point for each of your sentences.

_____

_____

_____

_____

_____

_____

_____

_____

_____

_____

_____

_____

_____

Key phrases

- Terrestrial television
- Independent Television Commission (ITC)
- A and B group sporting events
- Bidding for sports coverage
- Expands number of sports shown
- Extra events for a one-off payment
- Subscription television

2 — Now say how the media can influence people to take part in sport.

_____

_____

_____

_____

_____

_____

_____

_____

_____

Worksheet 4: Terrestrial and subscription television

Level B   **Student's Book pages 30–37**

Tasks

1 — Write a paragraph on how terrestrial and subscription television differ. Use some of the key phrases below as a starting point for each of your sentences.

_____

_____

_____

_____

_____

_____

_____

_____

_____

_____

_____

_____

_____

Key phrases

- Terrestrial television
- Independent Television Commission
- A and B group sporting events
- Bidding for sports coverage
- Expands number of sports shown
- Extra events for a one-off payment

- Subscription television
- Inspire to play
- Want to regularly be a spectator
- Want to volunteer
- Want to coach

---

2 — Now say how the media can influence people to take part in sport.

_____

_____

_____

> Think of different types of roles in sport such as player, officials, coaches and volunteers.

_____

_____

_____

_____

_____

Worksheet 5: Experience different ways to enjoy sport

Level A   **Student's Book pages 29–30**

Tasks

1 — Read the partially completed sentences below.

2 — Complete the sentences using your knowledge and understanding of the different ways to enjoy and benefit from sport.

a) "Not only do we learn skills and rules in PE lessons, but also the way to live a _____

_____ too."

b) "We are taught many different activities in PE lessons. This has given me a _____

_____ from which to choose a leisure activity."

c) "Extra-curricular activities help me to improve my skills by providing _____

_____ to work on my favourite activities."

d) "Although I am not the captain of my school team, in lessons I have had the _____

_____ of my group."

e) "In the summer term _____ my own athletic results on the noticeboard from the teacher's records made in class."

f) "Especially in gymnastics and dance, I have the opportunity to _____

_____, teach them to others and perform them too."

g) "In class I learn the coaching points of different sports and am given the opportunity to practise instructing others to improve their performance. This improves my own _____."

h) "There are times when I have the chance to be the referee or umpire in class. This _____

_____ of the game and builds my confidence dealing with others."

Worksheet 5: Experience different ways to enjoy sport

Level B **Student's Book pages 29–30**

Tasks

1 — Read the partially completed sentences below.

2 — Use the statement bank to complete the following sentences on school and participation in sport. Each statement is used only once.

a) "Not only do we learn skills and rules in PE lessons, but also the way to live a _____ _____ too."

b) "We are taught many different activities in PE lessons. This has given me a _____ _____ from which to choose a leisure activity."

c) "Extra-curricular activities help me to improve my skills by providing _____ _____ to work on my favourite activities."

d) "Although I am not the captain of my school team, in lessons I have had the _____ _____ of my group."

e) "In the summer term _____ my own athletic results on the noticeboard from the teacher's records made in the class."

f) "Especially in gymnastics and dance, I have the opportunity to _____ _____, teach them to others and perform them too."

g) "In class I learn the coaching points of different sports and am given the opportunity to practise instructing others to improve their performance. This improves my own _____."

h) "There are times when I have the chance to be the referee or umpire in class. This _____ _____ of the game and builds my confidence of dealing with others."

Statement bank

- tests my knowledge of the rules
- compose my own routines
- broad range of experiences
- communication skills
- extra time
- healthy life
- experience of being the leader
- I am responsible for recording

Homework 1: Female role models

Student's Book pages 24–28

Task

Using Rebecca Adlington as an example, say why a company would want to use her for promotional purposes.

Use the following ideas to help you:

- What efforts has she made to achieve her state of fitness?
- What has she achieved?
- Where did she achieve it?
- What does her success mean to the country?
- What are her personal qualities?

Think about:

- The success of the athlete links with the success of the company/product
- A healthy athlete links with the healthy image of the company/product
- Integrity of the sportsperson gives integrity to the company/product
- Clean image of the sportsperson gives a clean image of the company/product.

_____

_____

_____

_____

_____

_____

_____

_____

_____

_____

_____

_____

_____

_____

_____

_____

_____

_____

_____

Homework 2: Men and sport

Student's Book page 23

Tasks

1 — Study the information below.

Boys often start playing sport because they regard the activity as great fun. In the controlled environment of a game situation an activity may provide an outlet for aggression and act as a release valve for youth, energy and enthusiasm. Sport can also provide opportunities to express natural tendencies for competition. Some sports are popular with men due to the nature of the game. For example, rugby attracts some males because it is a physically demanding contact sport.

LEISURE RUGBY UNION. Line-Out Action. HE. Photo: Chris Barry/Action Plus.

Activities readily available in a local area may have reputations for success because of good facilities, excellent coaching, social events and the like. These will be well known in the community and so new, young members (attracted by these reputations) will help keep the traditions and the strong continuation of the activity going in the area.

Training for an activity often develops skill, physique and competitiveness in sport and activities are often chosen by men for the physicality.

Men often state that their reason for joining a club is to be part of a team. They enjoy the feeling of togetherness and camaraderie brought about by being in a group of similarly minded people, all working to the same end. Many activities have a social side; teams will often have a clubhouse where everyone can mix after a game. Some clubs still have the tradition of providing a meal after a match for the players. When the speeches are over all the players can have a drink together and this gives the possibility of making new acquaintances and friends. Many clubs often arrange special social events enabling all members and friends to be involved and feel part of the club.

2 — Go back through the information and underline the main points – use the statement bank to help you.

3 — Create a spider diagram of the key points that suggests why males participate in sport.

Statement bank

- physical activity is fun
- acts as a release valve
- opportunities to express natural competitiveness
- enjoys the physicality
- opportunities to socialize with others
- keep traditions of the game and its standards going
- to be a member of a team

Extension 1: The sports participation pyramid

Student's Book pages 48–49

Tasks

1 — Study the diagram below of the sports participation pyramid.

Olympic, Paralympic and Commonwealth Games,
World, European and Commonwealth
championships and international competitions — **Elite**

Local and regional coaching and training,
local and regional competitions,
sports clubs and interclub leagues — **Performance**

Sports clubs and leisure centres — **Participation**

PE and recreational sports — **Foundation**

2 — For each section state:

- where participation in physical activity is likely to take place
- what age group will be involved
- what level of performance/competition is at each stage.

Use the statement bank to help you.

Statement bank

- School/leisure centres/fitness clubs
- Regional centres
- Fitness centres
- Regional training centres
- About 16+
- National centres of excellence
- Competition at regional level
- Coaching, training and competition at national level
- International training centres
- About 16+
- Recreational activity
- Physical Education in schools

- Leisure clubs
- Local training centres
- School
- Local clubs
- About 5–16
- School
- Coaching and training at regional level
- National centres of excellence
- International centres of excellence
- About 11–18
- Competition at international level

Extension 2: Joining a sports club

Student's Book page 52

Tasks

1 — Using your knowledge of joining a club, complete the following questions.

a) State three ways in which you could find out information about sports clubs in your area.

_____

_____

_____

_____

_____

_____

b) List four sports clubs in your area.

_____

_____

_____

_____

_____

_____

_____

2 — Choose one of the sports clubs and answer the following questions:

a) State two reasons why you chose that club.

_____

_____

_____

_____

b) What equipment would you need to buy in order to participate?

_____

_____

_____

_____

c) What equipment is provided for by the club?

_____

_____

_____

_____

Extension 3: Different roles in sport: clubs and committees

Student's Book pages 45–48

Tasks

1 — Link the committee members listed below with the appropriate job description at the foot of the page.

2 — Now write, in full sentences, the role and duties of each club member.

Committee members:

Results secretary _____

_____

_____

Governing body/council representative _____

_____

_____

Captain/vice captain _____

_____

_____

Secretary _____

_____

_____

Chairperson _____

_____

_____

Treasurer _____

_____

_____

Community officer _____

_____

_____

Job descriptions

- Keep check on club finances
- Record meetings
- Play in a full range of games in a season
- Inform of scores and league position
- Create links with various groups
- Run and keep order in a meeting
- Represent the players in meetings

1.1 Healthy, active lifestyles

1.1.3 Exercise and fitness as part of your healthy, active lifestyle

Contents

Worksheets

Homework sheet

Extension sheets

Worksheet 1: Sporting activities and health-related exercise

Level A   **Student's Book pages 60–62**

Tasks

1 — List the positive effects of having well-developed health-related exercise components in sport. Give an answer for each of the components of health-related exercise. Think about the different types of sporting activity there are. The pictures may help as a start.

_____

_____

_____

_____

_____

_____

_____

_____

_____

_____

_____

_____

_____

2 — Give the negative effects of not having well-developed health-related exercise components in sport. Give an answer for each of the components of health-related exercise. Think about the different types of sporting activity there are. The pictures may help as a start.

_____

_____

_____

_____

_____

_____

_____

_____

_____

_____

_____

_____

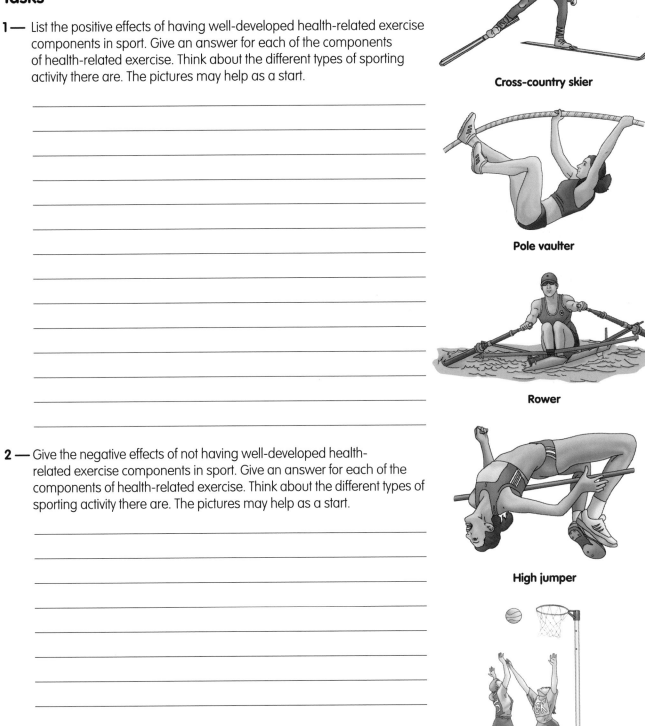

Cross-country skier

Pole vaulter

Rower

High jumper

Netball goalkeeper

Worksheet 1: Sporting activities and health-related exercise

Level B   Student's Book pages 60–62

Tasks

1 — In the table below, list the components of health-related exercise in the first column.

2 — Fill in the rest of the table with the positive and negative effects of each health-related exercise component. Give a sporting example for each.

> Use the information in the Student's Book and the illustrations on this page to help you.
>
> Use the same sport for your positive and negative examples.

An example has been given to help you.

Cross-country skier

Pole vaulter

Rower

High jumper

Netball goalkeeper

Component	Positive effects	Negative effects	Sport
Cardiovascular fitness	The body can meet the demands of exercise and keep working without losing skill.	Body cannot transport oxygen to the working muscles so they tire easily before the end of the race.	Skiing

1.1.3 Exercise and fitness as part of your healthy, active lifestyle

Worksheet 2: Components of skill-related fitness

Level A   **Student's Book pages 63–66**

Tasks

1 — Write in the correct component of skill-related fitness to match the following definitions:

a) The ability to apply a combination of strength and speed in an action: _____

b) The ability to change direction quickly and still keep control of the whole body: _____

c) The ability to keep the body stable whether still, moving or in a different shape by keeping the centre of gravity over the base: _____

d) The time it takes to respond to a stimulus: _____

e) The fastest rate a person can complete a task or cover a distance: _____

f) The ability to use two parts of the body at the same time: _____

2 — For each of the sports illustrated below, list the three most important components of skill-related fitness in the spaces provided.

1. _____   1. _____   1. _____

2. _____   2. _____   2. _____

3. _____   3. _____   3. _____

1. _____   1. _____   1. _____

2. _____   2. _____   2. _____

3. _____   3. _____   3. _____

Worksheet 2: Components of skill-related fitness

Level B   **Student's Book pages 63–66**

Tasks

1 — Write in the correct component of skill-related fitness to match the following definitions. Use the word bank to help you.

a) The ability to apply a combination of strength and speed in an action: _____

b) The ability to change direction quickly and still keep control of the whole body: _____

c) The ability to keep the body stable whether still, moving or in a different shape by keeping the centre of gravity over the base: _____

d) The time it takes to respond to a stimulus: _____

e) The fastest rate a person can complete a task or cover a distance: _____

f) The ability to use two parts of the body at the same time: _____

2 — For each of the sports illustrated below, list the three most important components of skill-related fitness: balance, reaction time, speed, agility, power and coordination.

1. _____

2. _____

3. _____

    1. _____

    2. _____

    3. _____

    1. _____

    2. _____

    3. _____

1. _____

2. _____

3. _____

    1. _____

    2. _____

    3. _____

    1. _____

    2. _____

    3. _____

1.1.3 Exercise and fitness as part of your healthy, active lifestyle

© Folens (copiable page)

Worksheet 3: Skilled performance

Level A   **Student's Book pages 63–66**

Tasks

1 — From your understanding of skilled performance, complete the table below by adding the definitions of the words in bold:

Efficiency	Pre-determined	Coordinated	Fluent	Aesthetic

2 — Choose six sporting examples where you have seen skilled performance.

_____

_____

_____

_____

_____

_____

3 — Develop four of these ideas into sentences.

_____

_____

_____

_____

_____

_____

_____

_____

_____

_____

_____

_____

_____

_____

Worksheet 3: Skilled performance

Level B   **Student's Book pages 63–66**

Tasks

1 — From your understanding of skilled performance, complete the table below by adding the definitions of the words in bold. Use the statement box to guide your answers.

> Use your workbook notes to help you.

Efficiency	Pre-determined	Coordinated	Fluent	Aesthetic

Statement bank

- Skills are fluent
- Control small muscle groups
- Minimal effort
- Skills are practiced
- Skills performed in predicted situations
- Skills are graceful
- Minimal thought

- Skills are performed with ease
- Practise equals maximum certainty of success
- Minimal time
- Combined use of muscles in complex skill
- Control large muscle groups
- Whole action looks good

2 — Choose four sporting examples where you have seen skilled performance.

_____

_____

_____

_____

_____

3 — Develop three of these ideas into sentences. Use the statement box to help you.

_____

_____

_____

_____

_____

Homework 1: Effects of health-related exercise on skill-related fitness

Student's Book pages 60–66

Tasks

1 — Study the components of health-related exercise and skill-related fitness.

2 — Using the illustrations as a starting point, give three sporting examples of how health-related exercise components can affect skill-related fitness components.

Here is an example:
Cardiovascular fitness: at the end of a long match or extra time, poor cardiovascular fitness will affect the muscles as oxygen cannot be taken up by the working muscles leading to poor coordination/reaction-time.

_____

_____

_____

_____

_____

_____

Health-related exercise	
• cardiovascular fitness	• flexibility
• muscular strength	• body composition
• muscular endurance	

Skill-related fitness	
• agility	• power
• balance	• reaction time
• coordination	• speed

1.1.3 Exercise and fitness as part of your healthy, active lifestyle

Extension 1: Health-related exercise and sports

Student's Book pages 60–62

Tasks

1 — Study the components of health-related exercise listed below:

- cardiovascular fitness
- muscular endurance
- muscular strength
- flexibility
- body composition

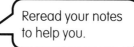
Reread your notes to help you.

2 — For each sportsperson illustrated, give a mark out of ten in the table below indicating how important that component is to the sport. Range your marks from 10 = most important to 0 = least important.

An athlete has been completed for you as a guide.

	Sprinter	Gymnast	Marathon runner	Hockey player
Cardiovascular fitness			8	
Muscular endurance			10	
Muscular strength			0	
Flexibility			6	
Body composition			9	

3 — On the back of this sheet, write a sentence on each component of health-related exercise for each of the sports illustrated, giving reasons for your mark allocations.

1.1.3 Exercise and fitness as part of your healthy, active lifestyle

Extension 2: Health-related exercise components

Student's Book pages 60–62

Tasks

1 — Study the part sentences below which relate to health-related exercise and skill-related fitness components.

2 — Choose what you think is the correct ending of the sentence from the statement bank and write your answer in the space provided.

> There are many options so choose carefully!

a) Flexibility is the body's ability to _____

_____

_____

b) A person with good muscular endurance can work their muscles over long

periods of time without _____

_____

_____

c) Muscular strength can be defined as the muscles' ability to _____

_____

_____

d) Good cardiovascular fitness will enable the heart and lungs to _____

_____

_____

e) Body composition _____

_____

_____

Statement bank

- tiring, losing effectiveness or reaching their maximum effort load.
- move the joints to the full range of movement.
- complete a task or cover a distance.
- respond to a shot or cover a distance.
- keeping control of their body when avoiding a tackle.
- body's content of bone, muscle and fat.
- supply oxygen to the working muscles over long periods of time.
- is the fastest rate a person can complete a task or cover a distance.
- apply force and overcome resistance.
- get distance on the throw.

3 — Link the sporting examples shown in the illustrations with each component of health-related exercise.

1.1 Healthy, active lifestyles

1.1.4a Physical activity as part of your healthy, active lifestyle: training principles and goal setting

Contents

Worksheets

Homework sheet

Extension sheets

Worksheet 1: Principles and planning

Level A   **Student's Book pages 68–74**

Tasks

1 — Write down the reasons why training principles are important to the performer.

> Think about the needs/requirements/skills of the sport.
>
> At what level will you start the training?
>
> How will you know to increase the intensity of the training?

_____

_____

_____

_____

_____

_____

_____

_____

_____

2 — What considerations should be made when creating a training schedule? Use the statement bank to help you.

_____

_____

_____

_____

_____

_____

_____

_____

Frequency
Intensity
Time
Type

Specificity
Progressive overload
Individual difference/needs
Rest and recovery

_____

_____

_____

_____

Statement bank

- The build of a person
- Personal reasons for exercising
- The height of a person
- A person's state of health
- Understanding of the body's systems
- The time of day
- Knowing how to apply the principles safely

1.1.4a Physical activity as part of your healthy, active lifestyle: training principles and goal setting

Worksheet 1: Principles and planning

Level B   **Student's Book pages 68–74**

Tasks

1 — Write down the reasons why training principles are important to the performer. Use the ideas box to help you.

> Use the notes you've made in your workbook to also help you.

Frequency
Intensity
Time
Type

Specificity
Progressive overload
Individual difference/needs
Rest and recovery

_____

_____

_____

_____

_____

_____

_____

_____

_____

Ideas box

- Are specific to the activity
- Help plan for progress
- Based on individual needs
- Shows how to progress further

2 — What considerations should be made when creating a training schedule? Select statements from the statement bank to help with your answers.

_____

_____

_____

_____

_____

_____

_____

_____

_____

Statement bank

- The build of a person
- Personal reasons for exercising
- The height of a person
- A person's state of health
- Understanding of the body's systems
- The time of day
- Knowing how to apply the principles safely

1.1.4a Physical activity as part of your healthy, active lifestyle: training principles and goal setting   © Folens (copiable page)

Worksheet 2: Classifying principles

Level A   **Student's Book pages 68–72**

Tasks

1 — Study the principles of training in the speech bubble.

2 — Read the list of key phrases below and match each one with a principle of training by placing the appropriate initial in the box by the phrase.

	Muscular strength is improved by matching the actions of the game/event.
	The exercise is performed above the threshold of training.
	Further training has to be planned.
	Exercise matches the actions of the sport.
	Effects of training are lost three times faster than any gain made.
	After six weeks, training changes to become harder.
	Exercise becomes more intense by increasing the frequency, intensity and time.
	Changes made to the programme are gradual to avoid injury.
	Muscle tissue and cells have time to repair.
	Injury or illness can stop training and so the athlete loses fitness.
	Training is at the pace of a competitive game.
	If training stops, muscles atrophy.
	Training programmes are designed around a person's fitness and needs.
	Body works harder than normal.

3 — Using the key phrases as a guide, write three sentences for each principle in the space provided. Use the back of this sheet if you need extra space.

_____

_____

_____

_____

_____

_____

_____

_____

_____

_____

_____

_____

_____

The speech bubble contains:
Specificity
Progressive overload
Individual differences/needs
Rest and recovery

Worksheet 2: Classifying principles

Level B   **Student's Book pages 68–72**

Task

1 — Read the statements a to n about the principles of training.

2 — Each statement is about one principle of training. Write the correct principle after each statement.

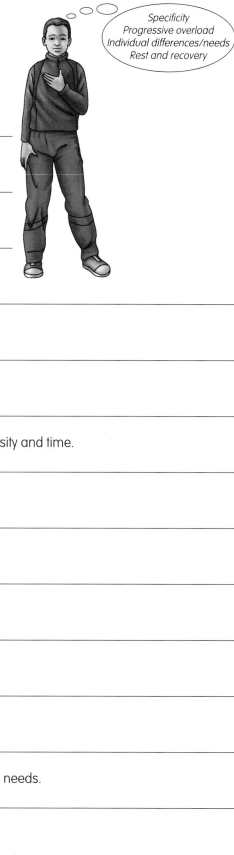

Specificity
Progressive overload
Individual differences/needs
Rest and recovery

a) Muscular strength is improved by matching the actions of the game/event.

_____

b) The exercise is performed above the threshold of training.

_____

c) Further training has to be planned.

_____

d) Exercise matches the actions of the sport.

_____

e) Effects of training are lost three times faster than any gain made.

_____

f) After six weeks, training changes to become harder.

_____

g) Exercise becomes more intense by increasing the frequency, intensity and time.

_____

h) Changes made to the programme are gradual to avoid injury.

_____

i) Muscle tissue and cells have time to repair.

_____

j) Injury or illness can stop training and so the athlete loses fitness.

_____

k) Training is at the pace of a competitive game.

_____

l) If training stops, muscles atrophy.

_____

m) Training programmes are designed around a person's fitness and needs.

_____

n) Body works harder than normal.

_____

50

Worksheet 3: The FITT principle

Level A   Student's Book pages 72–73

Tasks

1 — Answer the following questions.

I must apply FITT to my training in order to improve.

a) What does the F in FITT stand for? _____

b) What does the I in FITT stand for? _____

c) What does the first T in FITT stand for? _____

d) What does the second T in FITT stand for? _____

e) Which principle tells us that the training exercise should match the sporting action? _____

f) If a person usually trains three times per week but changes to training four times, which letter of FITT is affected? _____

g) What does 'progressive overload' mean to the person training?

_____

_____

_____

h) At what percentage of the maximum should a person train to, to apply the principle of progressive overload?

_____

2 — Fill in the gaps in the following sentences about reaching levels of fitness.

To achieve the minimum level of fitness, a person should follow these guidelines:

a) A person must train _____ times a week.

b) Training should last for at least _____ minutes.

c) The heart rate should rise to between _____ of the maximum heart rate.

d) To reach higher levels of fitness an athlete must train harder. A top-class athlete should train to _____ of their maximum to reach a performance to suit the level of competition.

e) Systematic programming is a planned change to the sessions applying the principle of _____.

f) Reversibility happens when training stops and the muscles _____.

g) Getting the right balance in the amount of training is called _____.

Worksheet 3: The FITT principle

Level B   **Student's Book pages 72–73**

Tasks

1 — Answer the following questions.

a) What does the F in FITT stand for? _____

b) What does the I in FITT stand for? _____

c) What does the first T in FITT stand for? _____

d) What does the second T in FITT stand for? _____

e) Which principle tells us that the training exercise should match the sporting action? _____

f) If a person usually trains three times per week but changes to training four times, which letter of FITT is affected? _____

g) What does the term 'progressive overload' mean to the person training?

_____

_____

_____

_____

h) At what percentage of the maximum should a person train to, to apply the principle of progressive overload? _____

> I must apply FITT to my training in order to improve.

2 — Fill in the gaps in the following sentences about reaching levels of fitness using the statement bank to help you.

To achieve the minimum level of fitness, a person should follow these guidelines:

a) A person must train _____ times a week.

b) Training should last for at least _____ minutes.

c) The heart rate should rise to between _____ of the maximum heart rate.

d) To reach higher levels of fitness an athlete must train harder.
A top-class athlete should train to _____ of their maximum to reach a performance to suit the level of competition.

e) Systematic programming is a planned change to the sessions applying the principle of _____.

f) Reversibility happens when training stops and the muscles _____.

g) Getting the right balance in the amount of training is called _____.

Statement bank	
• 20	• moderation
• 60–80 per cent	• atrophy
• five	• 80 per cent
• progressive overload	

1.1.4a Physical activity as part of your healthy, active lifestyle: training principles and goal setting   © Folens (copiable page)

Worksheet 4: SMART

Level A **Student's Book page 75**

Tasks

1 — Read and study the information below. It is an example of a sprinter's adaptation of the SMART goal setting.

S   To take a second off my time.

M   I shall time myself after five weeks of training.

A   My coach and I devised the training programme around improving leg strength and power, and reactions for my start.

R   We agreed that a second off my personal best is achievable.

T   We agreed to do the training programme four times per week for the next five weeks.

2 — Choose your own sport.

3 — Adapt the SMART goal setting to match your choice of sport.

S _____

_____

M _____

_____

A _____

_____

R _____

_____

T _____

_____

4 — State how your own goal setting will improve your performance. Remember, goal setting should achieve the following:

- optimize performance
- ensure exercise adherence
- control anxiety.

_____

_____

_____

_____

_____

_____

_____

_____

_____

Worksheet 4: SMART

Level B   Student's Book page 75

Tasks

1 — Read and study the information below. It is an example of a sprinter's adaptation of the SMART goal setting.

Remember SMART stands for:

S – Specific
M – Measurable
A – Achievable
R – Realistic
T – Time-bound

S To take a second off my time.

M I shall time myself after five weeks of training.

A My coach and I devised the training programme around improving leg strength and power, and reactions for my start.

R We agreed that a second off my personal best is achievable.

T We agreed to do the training programme four times per week for the next five weeks.

2 — Choose your own sport.

3 — Adapt the SMART goal setting to match your choice of sport.

S _____

_____

M _____

_____

A _____

_____

R _____

_____

T _____

_____

4 — State how your own goal setting will improve your performance. Remember, goal setting should achieve the following:

- optimize performance
- ensure exercise adherence
- control anxiety.

_____

_____

_____

_____

_____

_____

_____

_____

Homework 1: Principle of progressive overload

Student's Book pages 68–69

Tasks

1 — Read the paragraph below.

Progressive overload

During physical activity the body is gradually worked _____, this

is progressive overload. When the session is adapted to apply greater intensity, the changes should be

_____. Any increased workload must reach the _____,

which demands that the heart rate works above 60 per cent of its maximum. When applying progressive

overload to a training session, the _____ principles apply. The initials

stand for Frequency, Intensity, Time and Type. The amount of sessions undertaken per week relates to

_____. _____ the activity is concerns the intensity.

The _____ is to do with time. The activities performed in the session

are linked with _____.

2 — Fill in the gaps in the paragraph using the words from the statement bank.

Statement bank
• more than usual   • frequency
• length of the session   • type
• threshold of training   • FITT
• how difficult   • gradual

Extension 1: Three principles

Student's Book pages 68–74

Task

Read the paragraphs below and fill in the gaps with the words from the statement bank. Each statement is used once. The correct number of letter spaces are given for each answer.

Specificity

This principle relies on the activity _ _ _ _ _ _ _ _ _ the actions used in the game. They must be performed in the

_ _ _ _ _ _ _ and at the _ _ _ _ _ _ _ _ _ as the competition. If the skills are practised too slowly then

only _ _ _ _ _ _ _ _ _ _ _ _ _ _ _ _ _ will be reproduced. For specific skilled activities such as cycling

there is _ _ _ _ _ _ _ _ _ _ _ _ _ _ _ _ _ _ activity for the competitor – a cyclist's best training is cycling.

Progressive overload

When the body is gradually worked _ _ _ _ _ _ _ _ _ _ _ _ _ _ , this is overload. The extra workload must

reach the _ _ _ _ _ _ _ _ _ _ _ _ _ _ _ _ _ _ _ which is above 60 per cent of the maximum heart rate.

The _ _ _ _ principle applies to progressive overload. The initials stand for frequency, intensity, time and type. How

often a training session is done relates to _ _ _ _ _ _ _ _ _ _ . _ _ _ _ _ _ _ _ _ _ _ _ _ – the activity is concerns

the intensity. The _ _ _ _ _ _ _ _ _ _ _ _ _ _ _ _ is to do with time. The activity performed is linked with

_ _ _ _ . By regularly performing the training session the body will _ _ _ _ _ _ _ _ _ _ _ _ _ _ _ _ . When this

happens the session needs to be made more _ _ _ _ _ _ _ _ _ on the athlete. By _ _ _ _ _ _ _ _ the athlete at the

beginning of the programme and then five or six weeks later, changes the body has made can be recorded. The session

can be _ to add the necessary changes. This will include small

differences to the FITT principles.

Reversibility

When _ _ _ _ _ _ _ _ _ _ _ _ _ _ the effects of exercise are lost. The muscles begin to _ _ _ _ _ _ _ ,

losing their _ _ _ _ _ _ _ _ _ _ _ _ _ . It takes _ _ _ _ _ _ _ _ to lose fitness than gain it.

Statement bank

- more than usual
- matching
- length of the session
- threshold of training
- testing
- same way
- systematically planned
- no better substitute
- training stops
- less time
- FITT
- actions at that pace
- same speed
- frequency
- How difficult
- type
- shape and tone
- improve and adjust
- demanding
- atrophy

Extension 2: Two principles

Student's Book pages 68–70

Task

1 — Read the list of statements in the statement bank. Each statement refers to either the principle of specificity or progressive overload.

Statement bank

- if the skills are practised too slowly then only actions at that pace will be reproduced.
- by regularly performing the training session, the body will improve and adjust.
- the session can be systematically planned to add the necessary changes.
- for specific, skilled activities, such as cycling, there is no substitute activity for the competitor.
- changes will include adjustments to FITT.
- by testing the athlete at the beginning of the programme and then five to six weeks later, changes the body has made can be recorded.
- this principle relies on the activity matching the actions used in the game.
- the actions must be performed in the same way and at the same speed as the competition.
- after weeks of successful training the sessions need to be made more demanding.

2 — Write each statement under the correct heading below.

Specificity

_____

_____

_____

_____

_____

_____

_____

_____

_____

_____

Progressive overload

_____

_____

_____

_____

_____

_____

_____

_____

Extension 3: Short test

Student's Book pages 68–76

Tasks

Read the questions numbered 1 to 7 carefully and attempt them without the help of the notes in your workbook.

1. What do the initials FITT stand for?

(4 marks)

2. Explain the effect the FITT principle has on training.

(4 marks)

3. What is the principle of progressive overload?

(1 mark)

4. For training to have an effect, the heart rate should rise above 60 per cent of its maximum. What is this called?

(1 mark)

5. a) When training stops, what happens to the muscles of the body?

(1 mark)

   b) What principle of training applies when training stops?

(1 mark)

6. At what percentage of their maximum heart rate do top-class athletes train?

(1 mark)

Total: 13 marks

1.1.4a Physical activity as part of your healthy, active lifestyle: training principles and goal setting   © Folens (copiable page)

1.1 Healthy, active lifestyles

1.1.4b Physical activity as part of your healthy, active lifestyle: assessing fitness and developing an exercise programme

Contents

Worksheets

Homework sheets

Extension sheets

Worksheet 1: Interval training

Level A **Student's Book pages 79–82**

Tasks

1 — Fill in the interval training example below for sprinting.

After a complete warm-up:	
Time	**Activity**
0–15 secs	bursts of sprints
15–60 secs	
60–75 secs	bursts of sprints
	slow running
120–135 secs	
135–180 secs	slow running
180–195 secs	
195–240 secs	
	bursts of sprints
255–435 secs	slow running between sets
Each set takes _____ to complete. The whole session repeats four sets of the above.	

2 — Answer the following questions.

a) What other activities can be used in interval training instead of sprinting?

_____

_____

b) Work out how long the whole session would last.

_____

_____

c) If this session is to be performed accurately, what equipment is essential?

_____

_____

1.1.4b Physical activity as part of your healthy, active lifestyle: assessing fitness and developing an exercise programme   © Folens (copiable page)

Worksheet 1: Interval training

Level B   Student's Book pages 79–82

Tasks

1 — Fill in the interval training example below for sprinting. Use the statement bank to help you. Each of the statements is only used once.

After a complete warm up:	
Time	**Activity**
0–15 secs	bursts of sprints
15–60 secs	
60–75 secs	bursts of sprints
	slow running
120–135 secs	
135–180 secs	slow running
180–195 secs	
195–240 secs	
	bursts of sprints
255–435 secs	slow running between sets

Each set takes _____ to complete. The whole session repeats four sets of the above.

Statement bank

- 7 minutes 15 secs
- slow running
- bursts of sprints
- bursts of sprints
- slow running
- 75–120 secs
- 240–255 secs

2 — Answer the following questions.

a) What other activities can be used in interval training instead of sprinting?

_____

_____

b) Work out how long the whole session would last.

_____

_____

c) If this session is to be performed accurately, what equipment is essential?

_____

_____

Worksheet 2: Circuit training

Level A   **Student's Book pages 84–85**

Tasks

1 — Look at the exercises below. They make up a general fitness circuit. In the second box, change the circuit from a general fitness circuit to a skill fitness circuit using the same exercises.

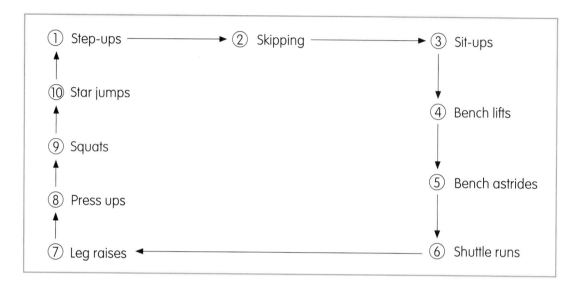

2 — Now create a circuit in your workbook, concentrating on a sport of your choice.

1.1.4b Physical activity as part of your healthy, active lifestyle: assessing fitness and developing an exercise programme   © Folens (copiable page)

Worksheet 2: Circuit training

Level B **Student's Book pages 84–85**

Tasks

1 — Look at the exercises below. They make up a general fitness circuit. In the second box, change the circuit from a general fitness circuit to a skill fitness circuit using the same exercises.

> Remember: change the muscle group used at the next station.

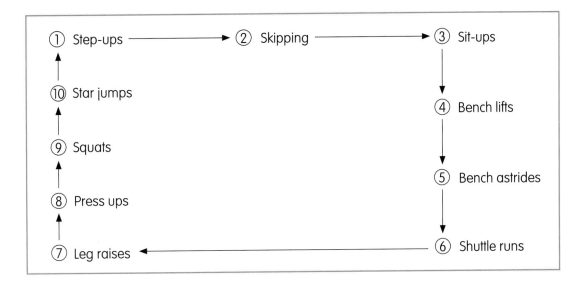

2 — Now create a circuit in your workbook, concentrating on a sport of your choice.

> Choose a sport.
> Choose skills from the game that are repeatable, in the same way, over again. Place them in the circuit.

Worksheet 3: Weight training

Level A   Student's Book pages 86–90

Tasks

1— Complete the paragraph below on weight training.

As a person works _____ on their weight session

their body becomes _____.

The session needs to be _____; these changes

are made _____ and _____. The

session will contain a series of _____ and _____. Sessions are made more

difficult in _____ ways: more _____ can be performed, more sets can be

_____ and extra _____ can be added to the lift.

2 — Read the statements below about free weight training and machine weight training.

Decide whether the statement goes under a free weights or a machine weights heading, or both, and write the correct headings next to each statement.

a) Needs specialized training: _____

b) Increases muscle size: _____

c) Not for beginners: _____

d) Easy to work: _____

e) Builds up strength: _____

f) Limit to the amount of weight lifted: _____

g) Injury due to poor technique: _____

h) Seats and belts make them safe: _____

i) Can help after injury: _____

j) Move only in the designed way: _____

k) Needs a spotter: _____

l) Use on your own: _____

m) Top sportspeople use them: _____

n) Uses anaerobic and aerobic respiration: _____

o) Easier to apply more weight: _____

p) Always set up and ready to use: _____

1.1.4b Physical activity as part of your healthy, active lifestyle: assessing fitness and developing an exercise programme

Worksheet 3: Weight training

Level B   Student's Book pages 86–90

Tasks

1 — Complete the paragraph below on weight training. Use the statement bank to help you.

As a person works _____ on their weight session

their body becomes _____.

The session needs to be _____; these

changes are made _____ and _____. The session will contain a series of

_____ and _____. Sessions are made more difficult in _____

ways: more _____ can be performed, more sets can be _____ and extra

_____ can be added to the lift.

```
┌─────────────────────────────────────────────────────────────────────┐
│                         Statement bank                              │
│                                                                     │
│   • adapted                        • regularly                      │
│   • repetitions                    • gradually                      │
│   • repetitions                    • three                          │
│   • sets                           • used to the weights            │
│   • weight                         • progressively                  │
│   • completed                                                       │
└─────────────────────────────────────────────────────────────────────┘
```

2 — Read the statements below comparing free weight training to machine weight training.

Decide whether each statement goes under a free weights (FW) or a machine weights (MW) heading, or both (B), and write the correct heading initials next to each statement. Several examples are given to help you.

a) Needs specialized training   FW

b) Increases muscle size   [B]

c) Not for beginners   [ ]

d) Easy to work   [M]

e) Builds up strength   [B]

f) Limit to the amount of weight lifted   [ ]

g) Injury due to poor technique   [ ]

h) Seats and belts make them safe   [ ]

i) Can help after injury   [B]

j) Move only in the designed way   [ ]

k) Needs a spotter   [ ]

l) Use on your own   [ ]

m) Top sportspeople use them   [ ]

n) Uses anaerobic and aerobic respiration   [ ]

o) Easier to apply more weight   [ ]

p) Always set up and ready to use   [ ]

Worksheet 4: Fartlek training

Level A **Student's Book pages 91–92**

Tasks

1 — Study the empty graph below. The y axis shows the athlete's heartbeats per minute. The x axis shows the time in minutes of a training session, starting with the warm-up and finishing with the cool-down.

Plot the following information on the empty graph.

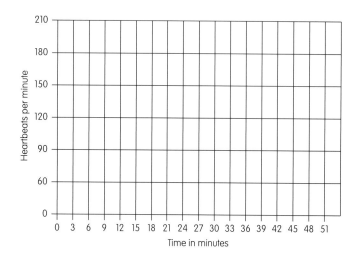

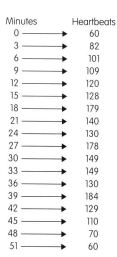

Minutes	Heartbeats
0	60
3	82
6	101
9	109
12	120
15	128
18	179
21	140
24	130
27	178
30	149
33	149
36	130
39	184
42	129
45	110
48	70
51	60

2 — Read the paragraphs below and fill in the spaces. Use the words from the word bank to help you.

The word Fartlek means _____ _____ in _____. Athletes can use _____,

_____ and _____ to run in. By using the natural changes in the countryside or beach the

demands on the athlete _____. Uphill work increases the _____ of the exercise and the heart

rate rises. Sprinting to marker trees or on sand dunes uses _____ _____. Periods of slower

running help the athlete to _____ so that training can continue and use the _____ _____

of respiration. The changes of intensity and time (duration) in the exercise _____ the demands of

_____ such as football or hockey. Therefore, games players find Fartlek training a good method to use.

Although running is commonly used, _____ and _____ also adapt to Fartlek training. As the

athlete's body _____ to the sessions, the training principles can be applied, so the session can still improve

fitness. Training more _____, at a _____ _____, for longer and with less _____

will keep the athlete _____. By making these changes the _____ principle is being applied.

Word bank

- match
- Swedish
- progressing
- hillsides
- recover
- aerobic system

- harder level
- adapts
- sand dunes
- speed play
- vary
- FITT

- cycling
- frequently
- woodland
- swimming
- rests
- games

- intensity
- anaerobic respiration

1.1.4b Physical activity as part of your healthy, active lifestyle: assessing fitness and developing an exercise programme © Folens (copiable page)

Worksheet 4: Fartlek training

Level B   **Student's Book pages 91–92**

Tasks

1 — Study the empty graph below. The y axis shows the athlete's heartbeats per minute. The x axis shows the time in minutes of a training session, starting with the warm-up and finishing with the cool-down.

Plot the following information on the empty graph.

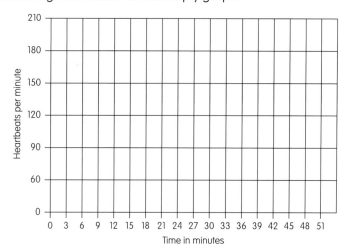

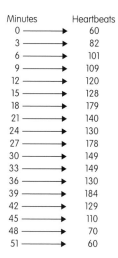

Minutes	Heartbeats
0	60
3	82
6	101
9	109
12	120
15	128
18	179
21	140
24	130
27	178
30	149
33	149
36	130
39	184
42	129
45	110
48	70
51	60

2 — Read the paragraphs below and fill in the spaces. Use the words from the word bank to help you. The first letters are given.

The word Fartlek means s_____ p_____ in S_____. Athletes can use

w_____, h_____ and s_____ to run in. By using the natural changes in

the countryside or beach the demands on the athlete v_____. Uphill work increases the

i_____ of the exercise and the heart rate rises. Sprinting to marker trees or on sand dunes uses

a_____ r_____. Periods of slower running help the athlete to r_____ so that

training can continue and use the a_____ of respiration. The changes of intensity and time

(duration) in the exercise m_____ the demands of g_____ such as football or hockey.

Therefore, games players find Fartlek training a good method to use.

Although running is commonly used, c_____ and s_____ also adapt to Fartlek training.

As the athlete's body a_____ to the sessions, the training principles can be applied, so the session

can still improve fitness. Training more f_____, at a h_____ l_____, for longer

and with less r_____ will keep the athlete p_____. By making these changes the

F_____ principle is being applied.

Word bank

- match
- Swedish
- progressing
- hillsides
- recover
- aerobic system
- harder level
- adapts
- sand dunes
- speed play
- vary
- FITT
- cycling
- frequently
- woodland
- swimming
- rests
- games
- intensity
- anaerobic respiration

---

et 5: Fartlek, cross and continuous

Student's Book pages 82–83 and 91–94

Tasks

1 — Study the illustrations below.

2 — In the space provided under each sportsperson write which method of training – Fartlek, cross or continuous – they are most likely to use.

3 — In the speech bubbles write what you think each person would say about their training method.

1.1.4b Physical activity as part of your healthy, active lifestyle: assessing fitness and developing an exercise programme   © Folens (copiable page)

Worksheet 5: Fartlek, cross and continuous training

Level B   **Student's Book pages 82–83 and 91–94**

Tasks

1 — Study the illustrations below.

2 — In the space provided under each sportsperson write which method of training – Fartlek, cross or continuous – they are most likely to use.

3 — In the speech bubbles write what you think each person would say about their training method. Use the statement bank to help you.

Statement bank

- "I like to vary the way I train."
- "I like to work on the rower and the stepper."
- "I enjoy training outside."
- "My general fitness is important to me."
- "I need to improve my cardiovascular systems training methods."
- "My event needs me to change speeds."
- "My joints are not what they used to be so I change activities to rest them."
- "I have good aerobic and anaerobic fitness."
- "I am exercising for my general health."

Worksheet 6: Personal Exercise Programme (PEP)

Level A   **Student's Book pages 97–98**

Tasks

1 — Study the statements below. Put the ideas into a logical order to design a Personal Exercise Programme (PEP). Number the boxes next to each statement from 1 to 10: 1 being the first part of the PEP.

Re-assess by checking the effects of the exercise on the original test results.

Assess the ability of the person in several areas by testing various skills.

Analyse test.

Take into account the experience of the person.

Find out how efficient the lungs are by working out the VO_2 max.

Take into account the age of the person.

Understand the pulse and find the resting pulse.

Set tasks for the subject.

Has the person got any training preferences?

What is the purpose of the training?

2 — Think about how you would design a PEP, either for yourself or for another student in your class. Answer the questions below for that person. Use the back of this sheet if you need more space.

a) What is the purpose of the training? _____

b) Is it for a particular sport? _____

c) How fit is the person training? _____

d) What is their resting pulse? _____

e) What is their VO_2 maximum? _____

f) What is their physical condition? _____

g) Where will they train? _____

h) Will they train on their own or with others? _____

i) Are there any results to record? _____

j) How will you assess their progress? _____

k) What is the physical condition of the person? _____

l) How will you review the programme? _____

m) If changes are to be made, how will you apply the principles of training? _____

1.1.4b Physical activity as part of your healthy, active lifestyle: assessing fitness and developing an exercise programme   © Folens (copiable page)

Worksheet 6: Personal Exercise Programme (PEP)

Level B   **Student's Book pages 97–98**

Tasks

1 — Study the statements below. Put the ideas into a logical order to design a Personal Exercise Programme (PEP). Number the boxes next to each statement from 1 to 10: 1 being the first part of the PEP.

> Two examples have been given to help you.

Re-assess by checking the effects of the exercise on the original test results. ☐

Assess the ability of the person in several areas by testing various skills. ☐

Analyse test. ☐

Take into account the experience of the person. ☐

Find out how efficient the lungs are by working out the VO_2 max. ☐

Take into account the age of the person. ☐

Understand the pulse and find the resting pulse. 5

Set tasks for the subject. ☐

Has the person got any training preferences? ☐

What is the purpose of the training? 1

2 — Think about how you would design a PEP, either for yourself or for another student in your class. Answer the questions below for that person. Use the back of this sheet if you need more space.

> Two examples have been given to help you.

a) What is the purpose of the training?   *General fitness level* _____

b) Is it for a particular sport?   *No, but I do play Badminton* _____

c) How fit is the person training? _____

d) What is their resting pulse? _____

e) What is their VO_2 maximum? _____

f) What is their physical condition? _____

g) Where will they train? _____

h) Will they train on their own or with others? _____

i) Are there any results to record? _____

j) How will you assess their progress? _____

k) What is the physical condition of the person? _____

l) How will you review the programme? _____

m) If changes are to be made, how will you apply the principles of training? _____

Worksheet 7: Warm-up

Level A **Student's Book pages 95–96**

Tasks

1 — a) Write three sentences giving reasons why a warm-up helps the performer.

_____

_____

_____

_____

_____

_____

_____

_____

_____

_____

A warm-up precedes all intensive work whether training or competing.

b) Choose a sport and give three examples of appropriate exercises that would be included in a warm-up.

_____

_____

_____

_____

_____

2 — Link each of the following statements to one of these headings: 'warm-up', 'main activity' and 'cool-down'. Write the correct heading after each statement.

a) Stretch the main muscles of the body to stop aching: _____

b) Put skills into practice: _____

c) Begin gradually: _____

d) As a member of a team, compete to win: _____

e) Gradually slow the body down by walking: _____

f) Slowly increase the intensity: _____

1.1.4b Physical activity as part of your healthy, active lifestyle: assessing fitness and developing an exercise programme © Folens (copiable page)

Worksheet 7: Warm-up

Level B   **Student's Book pages 95–96**

Tasks

1 — a) Write three sentences giving reasons why a warm-up helps the performer. Use the ideas in the box to help you.

_____

_____

_____

_____

_____

_____

_____

_____

_____

A warm-up precedes all intensive work whether training or competing.

Ideas box

- Prepares the body
- Concentrates the mind
- Practise basic skills
- Gradually increase the intensity to match the sport

b) List three types of exercises that would be included in a warm-up.

_____

_____

_____

_____

_____

_____

2 — Link each of the following statements to one of these headings: 'warm-up', 'main activity' and 'cool-down'. Write the correct heading after each statement.

> Think about the warm-up you do to prepare for sport.

a) Stretch the main muscles of the body to stop aching: _____

b) Put skills into practice: _____

c) Begin gradually: _____

d) As a member of a team, compete to win: _____

e) Gradually slow the body down by walking: _____

f) Slowly increase the intensity: _____

Worksheet 8: Testing protocol

Level A **Student's Book pages 97–98**

Task

Read each of the following paragraphs, study the word bank and fill in the gaps. Use your workbook if necessary.

Reliability

Being _____ and following the correct _____ for all tests, makes the test results reliable. This gives the chance for consistent results to be _____, used in the future and _____ with recognized norms.

The results depend on:

- How _____ the performer is to do their best in the test.
- Is the performer _____?
- How long is it since the performer's last _____ and the test?
- For tests taking place outside, then the _____ should be the same each time the test is carried out. The weather and _____ could change the surface and temperature, which in turn will affect results.

Validity

If the results are to be used _____, then the test's validity must be ensured:

- Does the test _____ what you want it to?
- Is it _____ to the competitive activity/event?
- Is it a true _____ of the performer's ability and will it be recorded and set against recognized results tables?

Comparison

If carried out in the same _____ each time, test results will be true and can be compared _____ with recognized norms. These results may then be compared with _____ results, those of other peers and the _____ norms.

Safety

Safety is an important consideration when _____ any test.

The following questions must be answered:

- Is the space _____, does it suit the test?
- Is the _____ suitable?
- Is the correct _____ being worn by the performer?
- Is the correct _____ available for use?
- Are the _____ conditions suitable?

Word bank

• reflection	• consistent	• recorded	• compared	• way	• measure
• conditions	• meal	• meaningfully	• motivated	• lighting	• correct
• conducting	• procedures	• equipment	• recognized	• clothing	• legitimately
• season	• tired	• relevant	• past	• surface	

1.1.4b Physical activity as part of your healthy, active lifestyle: assessing fitness and developing an exercise programme © Folens (copiable page)

Worksheet 8: Testing protocol

Level B   **Student's Book pages 97–98**

Task

1 — Read each of the following paragraphs, study the word banks for each section and fill in the gaps using the words from each section's word bank.

Reliability

Being _____ and following the correct _____ for all tests, makes the test

results reliable. This gives the chance for consistent results to be _____, used in the future and

_____ with recognized norms.

The results depend on:

- How _____ the performer is to do their best in the test.

- Is the performer _____?

- How long is it since the performer's last _____ and the test?

- For tests taking place outside, then the _____

  should be the same each time the test is carried out. The weather and _____ could change the surface and temperature, which in turn will affect results.

Word bank

- compared
- motivated
- procedures
- season
- consistent
- meal
- tired
- conditions
- recorded

Validity

If the results are to be used _____, then the test's validity must be ensured:

- Does the test _____ what you want it to?

- Is it _____ to the competitive activity/event?

- Is it a true _____ of the performer's ability and will it be recorded and set against recognized results tables?

Word bank

- meaningfully
- measure
- reflection
- relevant

Comparison

If carried out in the same _____ each time, test results will be true and

can be compared _____ with recognized norms. These results may

then be compared with _____ results, those of other peers and

the _____ norms.

Word bank

- legitimately
- recognized
- past
- way

Safety

Safety is an important consideration when _____ any test. The following questions must be answered:

- Is the space _____, does it suit the test?

- Is the _____ suitable?

- Is the correct _____ being worn by the performer?

- Is the correct _____ available for use?

- Are the _____ conditions suitable?

Word bank

- equipment
- lighting
- clothing
- surface
- conducting
- correct

Worksheet 9: Testing and measuring

Level A   **Student's Book pages 99–109**

Tasks

1 — Fill in the table below with the following information:

- A component of health-related exercise.
- The type of test.
- Which area of the body is being tested?
- The anatomical name for the area being tested.

Component of health-related exercise	Type of test	Area tested	Anatomical name for area tested

2 — Interpreting results: study the results sheet below and work out what the sheet is telling each performer by answering the questions below. Record your answers on another sheet of paper.

Name	Cardiovascular fitness: Cooper's 12-minute run test (m)	Muscular strength: Hand grip strength test (kg)	Cardiovascular fitness: Harvard step test (heart rate)	Muscular endurance: Treadmill test (km per hour)	Flexibility: Sit and reach test (cm)
Christopher	2700	66	91	9	16
Yogita	2000	27	78	6	18
William	2100	55	66	7	7
Dean	1100	42	42	3	–9
Lisa	1200	33	58	5	22

a) Select an individual's results and work out:

- Which is their best activity?
- Which areas need improving?
- Which exercises would help further improvement in these areas?

b) Who are the best performers in each activity?

c) Who is the best performer overall?

d) Which performer could make the most improvement?

1.1.4b Physical activity as part of your healthy, active lifestyle: assessing fitness and developing an exercise programme   © Folens (copiable page)

Worksheet 9: Testing and measuring

Level B   **Student's Book pages 99–109**

Tasks

1 — Fill in the table below with the following information:

- A component of health-related exercise.
- The type of test.
- Which area of the body is being tested?
- The anatomical name for the area tested.

Some boxes have been filled in to help you.

Component of health-related exercise	Type of test	Area tested	Anatomical name for area tested
Muscular strength			
	Cooper's 12-minute run test		
		Leg muscles	
			Latissimus dorsi and hamstrings

2 — Interpreting results: study the results sheet below and work out what the sheet is telling each performer by answering the questions below. Record your answers on another sheet of paper.

Name	Cardiovascular fitness: Cooper's 12-minute run test (m)	Muscular strength: Hand grip strength test (kg)	Cardiovascular fitness: Harvard step test (heart rate)	Muscular endurance: Treadmill test (km per hour)	Flexibility: Sit and reach test (cm)
Christopher	2700	66	91	9	16
Yogita	2000	27	78	6	18
William	2100	55	66	7	7
Dean	1100	42	42	3	–9
Lisa	1200	33	58	5	22

a) Select an individual's results and work out:

- Which is their best activity?
- Which areas need improving?
- Which exercises would help further improvement in these areas?

b) Who are the best performers in each activity?

c) Who is the best performer overall?

d) Which performer could make the most improvement?

Homework 1: Circuit training

Student's Book pages 84–85

Task

Circuit training is a method of training. Next to each of the following statements, note down whether they are an advantage [A] or disadvantage [D] of circuit training.

a) A circuit can be set for individual needs.

b) Top-class sportspeople cannot achieve a high enough level of skill.

c) Each person doing the circuit can have their own targets.

d) Beginners and fitter people can work at the same time.

e) It is difficult to check that all of the activities are performed properly.

f) It can develop both aerobic and anaerobic respiration.

g) When using large muscle groups at each station (moving the whole body), aerobic respiration is in operation and this will develop the cardiovascular system.

h) If exercising small muscle groups (such as the biceps and triceps) in turn at the stations, this is anaerobic and builds strength.

i) Minimum equipment is needed.

j) It can be performed alone or in a group.

 1.1.4b Physical activity as part of your healthy, active lifestyle: assessing fitness and developing an exercise programme   © Folens (copiable page)

Homework 2: Fartlek training

Student's Book pages 91–92

Tasks

1 — Cut out the pieces of the graph on Fartlek training at the bottom of this sheet and then put them together in the right order. When you have got it right, stick them onto a separate piece of paper with your name on it.

2 — Answer the following questions using the information from the reassembled graph.

a) What is the highest heart rate? _____

b) How long does the warm-up last/when does the heart rate reach 60 per cent of its maximum? _____

_____

c) How many times does the heart rate enter the training zone? _____

d) When do they occur in the session? _____

_____

e) How long does the Fartlek training session last? _____

f) How many resting periods are there in the session? _____

g) How can you tell a resting period? _____

_____

h) When do the resting periods occur? _____

i) Why is it important to have resting periods in the session? _____

_____

j) At what time does the session finish and the cool-down take place? _____

k) How long does the cool-down last? _____

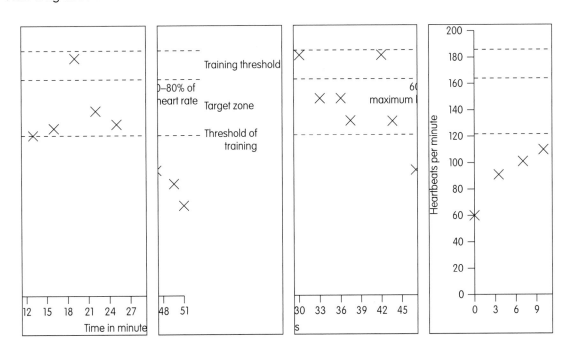

Homework 3: Cross training

Student's Book pages 92–94

Task

In the grids below, create a two-week programme for cross training. For each session, write in the activity, the duration (time in minutes) and the intensity (pulse rate).

> The following examples could be used:
> Activities: cycling, running, rowing, swimming, circuit training.
> Duration/time in minutes: 20, 60, 30, 30, 25 minutes.
> Frequency: plot on the timetable four sessions a week. Some activities can be duplicated.
> Intensity: each session should have a pulse rate of between 60 and 80 per cent of maximum heart rate.

Week one	Mon	Tues	Wed	Thurs	Fri	Sat	Sun
am							
lunch							
pm							

Week two	Mon	Tues	Wed	Thurs	Fri	Sat	Sun
am							
lunch							
pm							

1.1.4b Physical activity as part of your healthy, active lifestyle: assessing fitness and developing an exercise programme   © Folens (copiable page)

Extension 1: Interval training

Student's Book pages 79–82

Tasks

1 — Study the interval training pattern below for rowing. Note the seconds are accumulating and a full warm-up has been completed.

Accumulating seconds	Type of activity
0–15	Bursts of sprints
15–60	Slow rowing
60–75	Bursts of sprints
75–120	Slow rowing
120–135	Bursts of sprints
135–180	Slow rowing
180–195	Bursts of sprints
195–240	Slow rowing
240–255	Bursts of sprints
255–435	Slow rowing between sets

2 — Think about the speed changes and their timings.

3 — Adapt this type of training to suit the game of hockey using the table below.

Accumulating seconds	Type of activity

Extension 2: Circuit training

Student's Book pages 84–85

Tasks

1 — Study the circuit below for general fitness: note the order of the activities and the type of activities that follow each other.

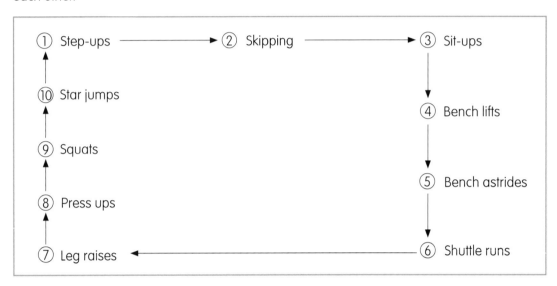

2 — Sarah is a keen skier. She has chosen circuit training to be part of her training programme. How can Sarah make this method work best for her? Draw out a ten-station circuit that Sarah feels confident will help her skiing.

Extension 3: Fartlek training

Student's Book pages 91–94

Task

Fartlek is Swedish for 'speed play'. A Fartlek training session involves exercises varying in time, distance and effort. In the space below, set out a training session for a cyclist, using the Fartlek method.

> Remember: When adapting Fartlek training to cycling the session would include using different gradients and gears.

> Start with a warm-up, then the main session, then the cool-down.

Time in minutes	Training

1.1 Healthy, active lifestyles

1.1.5 Your personal health and well-being

Contents

Worksheets

Homework sheet

Extension sheets

Worksheet 1: Nutrients

Level A   Student's Book pages 116–118

Tasks

Answer the following questions on nutrients, using the statement bank to help you.

1 — What is the major job of:

a) carbohydrates?_____

b) proteins?_____

c) fats?_____

d) vitamins?_____

2 — Give four examples of foods that contain:

a) vitamins: _____

b) carbohydrates: _____

c) proteins: _____

3 — How does the sportsperson use the following?

a) carbohydrates: _____

_____

b) proteins: _____

_____

c) water: _____

_____

d) fats:_____

_____

Statement bank

- meat
- maintaining general health
- liver
- instant energy provider
- nuts
- body builder and tissue repair
- bread
- stored energy

- fish
- fruit
- vegetable oils
- cakes
- pasta
- keep the balance of fluids in the body
- repair tissue after injury

- carrots
- as an insulator in extreme weather conditions
- beans
- carbohydrate loading for endurance events
- beer

---

4 — What two types of carbohydrates are there and in what form are they stored in the body?

_____

_____

_____

_____

Worksheet 1: Nutrients

Level B   **Student's Book pages 116–118**

Tasks

Answer the following questions on nutrients, using the statement banks to help you.

1 — What is the major job of:

a) carbohydrates? _____

b) proteins? _____

c) fats? _____

d) vitamins? _____

Statement bank

- Maintaining general health
- Instant energy provider
- Body builder and tissue repair
- Stored energy

2 — Give four examples of foods that contain:

a) vitamins: _____

b) carbohydrates: _____

c) proteins: _____

Statement bank

- meat
- pasta
- fish
- liver
- beans
- fruit
- carrots
- beer
- vegetable oils
- nuts
- cakes
- bread

3 — How does the sportsperson use the following?

a) carbohydrates: _____
_____

b) proteins: _____
_____

c) water: _____
_____

d) fats: _____
_____

Statement bank

- Keep the balance of fluids in the body
- Repair tissue after injury
- As an insulator in extreme weather conditions
- Carbohydrate loading for endurance events

4 — What two types of carbohydrates are there and in what form are they stored in the body?

_____

_____

_____

_____

_____

_____

_____

_____

Worksheet 2: Marathon runners and diet

Level A   **Student's Book pages 120–121**

Task

This task is about marathon runners and how they change their diet to give themselves the best results.

From your knowledge of marathon runners and their dietary habits, write a paragraph for each of the following headings on how they would adapt their eating habits to help them perform at their best.

a) Pre-event _____

_____

_____

_____

_____

_____

_____

b) Day of event _____

_____

_____

_____

_____

_____

_____

c) During the event _____

_____

_____

_____

_____

_____

_____

d) After the event _____

_____

_____

_____

_____

_____

_____

Worksheet 2: Marathon runners and diet

Level B   **Student's Book pages 120–121**

Task

This task is about marathon runners and how they change their diet to give themselves the best results.

Below is a list of various things a long-distance athlete might do to change their eating habits before, during and after an event. However, the list is not correctly sequenced.

Put the items in the list in the correct order so it follows a logical sequence. Number the items from 1 to 10 in the boxes provided.

> Some statements have a direct reference to timing, so put those down first and fit the others around them.

a) Fluids and energy drinks continue to be drunk. ☐

b) Carbohydrate loading continues the day before the race. Sometimes 'pasta parties' are organized. ☐

c) For the race, energy levels should be high, provided by carbohydrates. ☐

d) Two hours before the race, a small meal of carbohydrates is eaten. ☐

e) High-energy food is eaten immediately after the race. ☐

f) The intensive training makes carbohydrates low and proteins high in the athlete's body. ☐

g) During the race, fluids are regularly taken to stop dehydration. ☐

h) Five days before the race, training reduces and carbohydrate intake increases. ☐

i) Sports drinks, containing carbohydrates, are taken in the race to help the body work harder for longer. ☐

j) This change allows the body to store carbohydrates as glycogen. ☐

Worksheet 3: Sports and diet

Level A   Student's Book pages 114–120

Tasks

1 — Read each of the following statements and write the letter of the relevant sportsperson after it, choosing from the illustrations below.

a) "I need energy for the game so I eat a high carbohydrate/low fat diet, taking in plenty of fluids."

b) "Although I need upper body strength for my sport, my diet has a balance of all seven nutrients."

c) "I am recovering from a twisted knee injury caused by an opponent's stick tripping me, so I am on a diet with increased proteins helping repair the tissues in my knee."

d) "Keeping my weight down so I can make the weight is always a problem."

e) "In my sport I need to have strength and speed, so my diet has a combination of large amounts of proteins and carbohydrates."

f) "As much of my body tissue as possible needs to be muscle, so I eat a diet which is high in protein."

A. Rugby league player

B. Jockey

C. Footballer

D. Injured hockey player

E. Archer

F. Weight lifter

2 — Choose two different sports. On the other side of this sheet, write a sentence on each about a type of activity and a diet that would be suitable for it.

3 — On the other side of this sheet, write three facts about carbohydrate loading and three facts about high-protein diets.

Worksheet 3: Sports and diet

Level B **Student's Book pages 114–120**

Tasks

1 — Read each of the following statements and write the letter of the relevant sportsperson after it, choosing from the illustrations below.

a) "I need energy for the game so I eat a high carbohydrate/low fat diet, taking in plenty of fluids."

b) "Although I need upper body strength for my sport, my diet has a balance of all seven nutrients."

c) "I am recovering from a twisted knee injury caused by an opponent's stick tripping me, so I am on a diet with increased proteins helping repair the tissues in my knee."

d) "Keeping my weight down so I can make the weight is always a problem."

e) "In my sport I need to have strength and speed, so my diet has a combination of large amounts of proteins and carbohydrates."

f) "As much of my body tissue as possible needs to be muscle, so I eat a diet which is high in protein."

A. Rugby league player **B. Jockey** **C. Footballer**

D. Injured hockey player **E. Archer** **F. Weight lifter**

2 — Choose two different sports. On the other side of this sheet, write a sentence on each about a type of activity and a diet that would be suitable for it.

1.1.5 Your personal health and well-being   © Folens (copiable page)

Homework 1: Energy requirements

Student's Book page 115

Task

1 — Reorder the activities in Table A below, so that the activities with the highest energy requirements are at the top, working down to the lowest at the bottom. Note the new order in Table B.

2 — Convert the kilojoules into kilocalories, writing both in the appropriate column in Table B.

> One kilocalorie is equal to 4.2 kilojoules.
> To change from kilojoules to kilocalories, divide the number of kilojoules by 4.2.

Table A

Activities	Kilojoules (kJ)
Ice skating	376
Circuit training	1806
Weight lifting	676
Running	2033
Housework	790
Tennis	1579
Water aerobics	903
Mowing the lawn	1016
Gardening	1016
Swimming	1357
Cycling	1806
Walking	903

Table B

Activities (high-energy first)	Kilojoules (kJ)	Kilocalories (kcal)

Extension 1: Diet and the sportsperson

Student's Book pages 114–120

Task

From the list of foods in the word bank create the following three diets, listing them in the tables below:

a) An everyday balanced diet.

b) A diet for a long-distance athlete close to the time of their event.

c) A diet for a rugby player.

> In some cases, only small amounts of food are appropriate – please state when this is so. Think about the time of the event and what foods will help. Also think about the performer: which foods will help give them the right shape for their sport?

Word bank

- Toast
- Lamb chop
- Brown rice
- Grilled fish
- Pasta
- Lettuce
- Bacon
- Fried eggs
- Fruit
- Boiled potato
- Mashed potato
- Baked beans
- Tomatoes
- Cucumber
- Jacket potato
- Peas
- Sausages
- Carrots
- Cauliflower
- Cake
- Gammon ham
- Lean minced beef

An everyday balanced diet					
	Breakfast	Snack	Lunch	Snack	Dinner
Day 1					
Day 2					
Day 3					

A diet for a long-distance athlete close to the time of their event					
	Breakfast	Snack	Lunch	Snack	Dinner
Day 1					
Day 2					
Day 3					

A diet for a rugby player					
	Breakfast	Snack	Lunch	Snack	Dinner
Day 1					
Day 2					
Day 3					

1.1.5 Your personal health and well-being

Extension 2: Diet test

Student's Book pages 114–121

Tasks

Answer the following questions about diet. The marks available for each question are shown in brackets at the end of the question.

1 — List the seven nutrients needed by the body.

_____

_____

_____

(7 marks)

2 — To convert kilojoules (kJ) into kilocalories, divide the kilojoules by 4.2. Using this method, convert the figures below. Round up your answers to the nearest whole number.

a) 4200 kJ _____

b) 8900 kJ _____

c) 10,000 kJ _____

d) 11,200 kJ _____

(4 marks)

3 — How would the endurance athlete change their diet and training leading up to an event?

_____

_____

_____

_____

_____

(5 marks)

4 — What is the problem of using a high-protein diet?

_____

_____

_____

_____

(3 marks)

5 — How can being overweight affect a sportsperson?

_____

_____

_____

(4 marks)

Total: 23 marks

1.2 Your healthy, active body

1.2.1 Physical activity and your healthy mind and body

Contents

Worksheets

Homework sheets

Extension sheets

Worksheet 1: Somatotypes: body characteristics awareness

Level A   **Student's Book pages 129–130**

Tasks

1 — Which somatotype are each of the following athletes? They are either ectomorph (relatively thin), mesomorph (relatively muscled) or endomorph (relatively fat).

a) Jockey _____

b) Centre in netball _____

c) Prop in rugby _____

d) Gymnast _____

e) Swimmer _____

f) Marathon runner _____

g) Sprinter _____

2 — Link a different sportsperson with each of the following statements they might use to describe themselves. To do this:

- Read each statement carefully.
- Look on the Internet and find photos of the different shaped sportspeople.
- Link the statement with your researched photograph.

> If there are some sports you know little about, ask your friends for help or do some research in the library.
> If you find a picture of the type of player, use your judgement to decide the somatotype.

a) "I am medium build and am quick and strong." _____

b) "I am built like a greyhound – tall, sleek and with no fat on my body." _____

c) "I have a medium frame and my muscles are well-defined. I rely on speed and power for my sport."

_____

d) "I have no fat on my body and my build is small." _____

e) "I am medium build, strong and have no fat on my body." _____

f) "I am medium build, strong and with a lot of bulk so it is harder to push me over."

_____

g) "I carry no extra weight on my body, my muscles are sinewy and I am of medium build."

_____

Worksheet 1: Somatotypes: body characteristics awareness

Level B   **Student's Book pages 129–130**

Tasks

1 — Which somatotype are each of the following athletes? They are either ectomorph (relatively thin), mesomorph (relatively muscled) or endomorph (relatively fat).

a) Jockey _____

b) Centre in netball _____

c) Prop in rugby _____

d) Gymnast _____

e) Swimmer _____

f) Marathon runner _____

g) Sprinter _____

2 — Link a different sportsperson with each of the following statements they might use to describe themselves. Read each statement and write the correct sportsperson after it, from the list below.

> If there are some sports you know little about, ask your friends for help or do some research in the library.
> If you find a picture of the type of player, use your judgement to decide the somatotype.
> Use the word bank to help you.

a) "I am medium build and am quick and strong." _____

b) "I am built like a greyhound – tall, sleek and with no fat on my body." _____

c) "I have a medium frame and my muscles are well-defined. I rely on speed and

power for my sport." _____

d) "I have no fat on my body and my build is small." _____

e) "I am medium build, strong and have no fat on my body." _____

f) "I am medium build, strong and with a lot of bulk so it is harder to push me over."

_____

g) "I carry no extra weight on my body, my muscles are sinewy and I am of medium build."

_____

Word bank

- Jockey
- Centre in netball
- Prop in rugby
- Gymnast
- Swimmer
- Marathon runner
- Sprinter

1.2.1 Physical activity and your healthy mind and body   © Folens (copiable page)

Worksheet 2: Effects of drugs

Level A   **Student's Book pages 134–138**

Tasks

1 — Use the phrases from the statement bank to fill in the spaces in these sentences about the effects of drugs.

a) In _____ sports, smoking can affect the circulation of the blood around the body and can cause heart problems in later life. It can, however, _____ and so appear to improve performance in target sports.

b) Alcohol is a _____ drug. In sufficient quantities it can _____ and combined with sport can be dangerous.

c) Diuretics can be used as a _____ to hide the presence of other drugs.

d) Beta-blockers slow the heart rate, lower blood pressure and so are used _____. They are banned in sports that require _____, such as snooker.

e) Anabolic steroids mimic the male hormone testosterone, increasing _____ and _____ and muscle strength. Despite the damaging side effects, the drug helps the performer to _____.

Statement bank

- physically demanding
- masking agent
- calm the nerves
- as a relaxant

- a steady hand and a calm nerve
- muscle size
- bone growth

- recover from injury quickly
- impair judgement
- socially acceptable

---

2 — Write down eight reasons why a sportsperson may be tempted to take drugs to improve their sporting performance.

_____

_____

_____

_____

_____

_____

_____

Worksheet 2: Effects of drugs

Level B   **Student's Book pages 134–138**

Task

Use the phrases from the statement bank to fill in the spaces in these sentences about the effects of drugs.

a) In _____ sports, smoking can affect the circulation of the blood around the body and can cause heart problems in later life. It can, however,

_____ and so appear

to improve performance in target sports.

b) Alcohol is a _____ drug. In

sufficient quantities it can _____

and combined with sport can be dangerous.

c) Diuretics can be used as a _____ to

hide the presence of other drugs.

d) Beta-blockers slow the heart rate, lower blood pressure and so are used

_____. They

are banned in sports that require _____, such

as snooker.

e) Anabolic steroids mimic the male hormone testosterone, increasing _____

and muscle strength. Despite the damaging side effects, the drug helps the performer to

_____.

Statement bank

- physically demanding
- masking agent
- calm the nerves
- as a relaxant
- a steady hand and a calm nerve
- muscle size, bone growth
- recover from injury quickly
- impair judgement
- socially acceptable

Worksheet 3: Safety in sport

Level A　　　　**Student's Book pages 139–151**

Tasks

1 — Peter is responsible for the safety of the javelin, long jump and shot-put events in the forthcoming athletics meeting.

In the spaces provided below, describe what Peter must do to make each event safe.

Javelin: _____

_____

_____

_____

_____

_____

Long jump: _____

_____

_____

_____

_____

_____

Shot-put: _____

_____

_____

_____

_____

_____

2 — Yvonne has been asked to check the pool surround for safety before a school party arrives. List what could be checked.

> Use your knowledge and experience of your own athletic sports day events and swimming experience to help you.

_____

_____

_____

_____

_____

_____

_____

Worksheet 3: Safety in sport

Level B **Student's Book pages 139–151**

Tasks

1 — Peter is responsible for the safety of the javelin, long jump and shot-put events in the forthcoming athletics meeting. In the spaces provided below, describe what he must do to make each event safe.

Javelin: _____

_____

_____

_____

_____

_____

Long jump: _____

_____

_____

_____

_____

_____

Shot-put: _____

_____

_____

_____

_____

_____

_____

2 — Yvonne has been asked to check the pool surround for safety before a school party arrives. List what could be checked. Use the ideas box to help you.

_____

_____

_____

Ideas box
• Space for activity • Obstacles • Storage of equipment • Safety measures and equipment • Knowledge of participants

_____

_____

_____

_____

_____

Worksheet 4: Outdoor and adventurous activities

Level A **Student's Book pages 143–146**

Task

This task looks at the specialized safety equipment needed for some outdoor and adventurous activities.

For each of the activities listed in the table below:

- List two specialized pieces of safety equipment.
- Write a sentence for each piece of equipment about its safety function.

Activity	Specialized safety equipment	How the equipment makes the activity safe
Mountaineering		
Rock climbing		
Canoeing		
Sailing/windsurfing		
Orienteering		

Worksheet 4: Outdoor and adventurous activities

Level B   Student's Book pages 143–146

Task

This task looks at the specialized safety equipment needed for some outdoor and adventurous activities.

For each of the activities listed in the table below:
- List two specialized pieces of safety equipment.
- Write a sentence for each piece of equipment about its safety function.

A few answers have been completed already to help you.

> Use your own sporting experience, knowledge and the Internet to help you complete the rest.

Activity	Specialized safety equipment	How the equipment makes the activity safe
Mountaineering	Cagoule/waterproof jacket	Helps to keep the wearer dry and so reduce heat loss.
Rock climbing		
Canoeing		Helps to protect the head if the wearer capsizes.
Sailing/windsurfing	Wetsuit	
Orienteering	Whistle	

1.2.1 Physical activity and your healthy mind and body   © Folens (copiable page)

Worksheet 5: Safety rules

Level A   **Student's Book page 151**

Tasks

1 — Write down four jobs that a referee does, concerning rules, players and safety.

_____

_____

_____

_____

_____

_____

_____

_____

_____

_____

_____

2 — Make a list of possible infringements in a game that could lead to poor behaviour or dangerous play. For each, give a rule that attempts to prevent the situation. Two examples have been provided to help you.

Rugby – player using abusive language – ten-yard rule – gives territory to the opposition.

Hockey – raising the stick dangerously above the head – sticks rule – gives a free hit to the opposition.

_____

_____

_____

_____

_____

_____

_____

_____

_____

_____

_____

_____

Worksheet 5: Safety rules

Level B   **Student's Book page 151**

Tasks

1 — Write down four jobs that a referee does, concerning rules, players and safety. Use the word bank to help you.

_____

_____

_____

_____

_____

_____

_____

_____

_____

_____

Word bank

- Control
- Fairness
- Keeps discipline
- Game is safe
- Keep players within rules

2 — Make a list of possible infringements in a game that could lead to poor behaviour or dangerous play. For each, give a rule that attempts to prevent the situation. Two examples have been provided to help you.

Use the following phrases to help you:
- personal conduct
- control of equipment
- performance of skills.

Rugby – player using abusive language – ten-yard rule – gives territory to the opposition.

Hockey – raising the stick dangerously above the head – sticks rule – gives a free hit to the opposition.

_____

_____

_____

_____

_____

_____

_____

_____

_____

_____

_____

_____

Homework 1: Hazards and playing areas

Student's Book pages 138–140

Tasks

1 — Study the illustration below.

2 — Identify 12 hazards on the illustration, using the ideas bank to help you.

3 — Record these hazards and link them with a potential injury they could cause.

Ideas bank
• Litter
• Personal presentation
• Balanced competition
• Mix of sports
• Condition of the area
• Spectators

_____

_____

_____

_____

_____

_____

_____

_____

_____

_____

_____

_____

Homework 2: Safety clothing and equipment

Student's Book pages 147–150

Task

Study the illustrations of the two sportspeople below, of an opening batsman in cricket and a hockey goalkeeper. On each picture, draw all the safety equipment required for their sport. List the safety equipment below each picture.

List of safety equipment:

_____

_____

_____

_____

_____

_____

_____

_____

_____

List of safety equipment:

_____

_____

_____

_____

_____

_____

_____

_____

_____

Extension 1: Somatotypes

Student's Book pages 129–130

Task

1 — Study the list of sportspeople below.

- Footballer
- Badminton player
- Hockey player
- Long-distance runner
- Sprinter
- Jockey
- Basketball player
- Gymnast
- Sumo wrestler

Think about:
- the movements the player has to make
- how long the event lasts
- is bulk/height an advantage?

2 — Place each of them in the table below which lists the somatotypes.

Ectomorph	Mesomorph	Endomorph

3 — Choose one example from each somatotype and say why their physical characteristics suit that sport.

_____

_____

_____

_____

_____

_____

_____

_____

_____

_____

Extension 2: Banned substances: the facts

Student's Book pages 135–138

Task

Using the information on drugs from your workbook notes or the Internet, fill in the table below. Some answers have been filled in already to help you.

	Drugs in this category	Which athlete would use this drug?	The effect on the athlete	Side effects/dangers
Anabolic steroids				Mood swings Men: impotence Women: infertility
Stimulants	Amphetamines Ephedrine Caffeine			
Diuretics		Jockey/boxer needing to make a certain weight		
Peptide hormones				
Beta-blockers			Calms, steadies the hands, slows heart rate down	
Narcotic analgesics				

1.2.1 Physical activity and your healthy mind and body

Extension 3: Safety and officiating

Student's Book pages 139–151

Tasks

1 — Jennifer has just agreed to officiate a competitive match. Choose the type of match she is to officiate in.

2 — Make a list below of all the checks she needs to make for the match.

> Think of checks to be made before, during and after the match.

Type of match:

_____

List of checks:

_____

_____

_____

_____

_____

_____

_____

_____

_____

_____

_____

_____

_____

_____

_____

_____

_____

_____

_____

Extension 4: Rules for safety, order and fairness

Student's Book pages 139–151

Tasks

1 — Read the table below. It describes decisions a referee could make during a game of rounders.

2 — Work out whether each decision is designed to improve safety, keep order or make play fair.

		Safety? Keeping order? Making play fair?
a)	Call 'no-ball' if the bowler's action is not continuous.	
b)	Call 'no ball' if the bowler bowls with the foot over the front line of the bowling square.	
c)	The ball passes the batter above the head or below the knee, or any bowl that hits the ground before reaching the batter.	
d)	Calls 'rounder' or 'half-rounder' after they score.	
e)	Gives any decisions concerning the front line of the batting square/back line of the batting square.	
f)	Gives decisions on 'backwards hits' and calls them when necessary.	
g)	Gives decisions on the first and fourth posts.	
h)	Gives decisions on all catches.	
i)	Calls the next player (by name or number) to the batting square.	
j)	Calls 'play' at the beginning of each innings.	
k)	Calls 'play' to restart the game after a dead ball situation.	
l)	Calls 'no-ball' for wide bowls/balls that hit or would have hit the player if they had not moved.	
m)	Bowls passing on the non-hitting side of the batter.	
n)	Give decisions on the second and third posts.	
o)	Call 'no-ball' if the bowler's foot goes over the back line of the bowling square.	
p)	Ensures the waiting batters and the out batters are behind their relevant lines.	

1.2.1 Physical activity and your healthy mind and body

1.2 Your healthy, active body

1.2.2 A healthy, active lifestyle and your cardiovascular system

Contents

Worksheets

Homework sheets

Extension sheets

Blank diagrams for labelling

Worksheet 1: Learning the parts of the circulatory system

Level A   **Student's Book pages 155–156**

Tasks

1 — Fill in all the labels on the diagram.

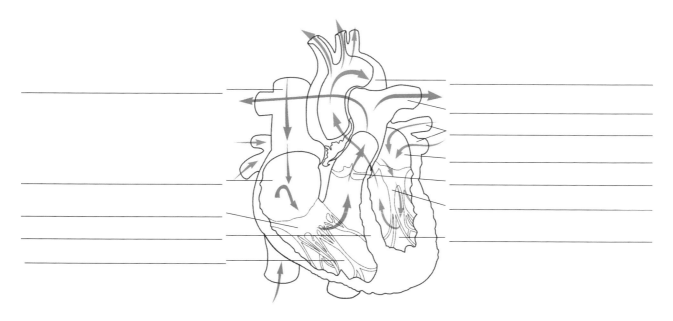

2 — Colour in the systemic and pulmonary systems. Remember that systemic systems carry blood from the heart to the rest of the body and back again. Pulmonary systems carry blood from the heart to the lungs and back.

3 — In your own words, write two paragraphs on the function of the cardiovascular system.

> Remember, the right side has the pulmonary artery taking deoxygenated blood away and the left side has the pulmonary vein bringing oxygenated blood back to the heart.

Worksheet 1: Learning the parts of the circulatory system

Level B   **Student's Book pages 155–156**

Tasks

1 — Fill in all the labels on the diagram, using words from the word bank.

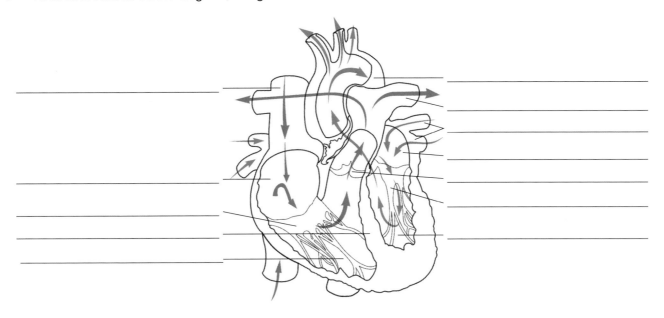

Word bank

Heart		**Blood vessels**	**Blood**
• Left atrium	• Mitral valve	• Pulmonary artery	• Oxygenated blood
• Right atrium	• Tricuspid valve	• Pulmonary vein	• Deoxygenated blood
• Left ventricle	• Semi-lunar valve	• Superior vena cava	
• Right ventricle	• Septum	• Aorta	

2 — Colour in the systemic and pulmonary systems. Remember that systemic systems carry blood from the heart to the rest of the body and back again. Pulmonary systems carry blood from the heart to the lungs and back.

> Remember, the right side has the pulmonary artery taking deoxygenated blood away and the left side has the pulmonary vein bringing oxygenated blood back to the heart.

Worksheet 2: The pathway of blood in the body

Level A   **Student's Book page 159**

Tasks

1 — Study the diagram. Track the pathway of blood in the body, starting at the heart leading into the pulmonary artery.

2 — Complete the table below by listing a part of the circulatory system and the pathway the blood takes. Three of the items have been completed to help you.

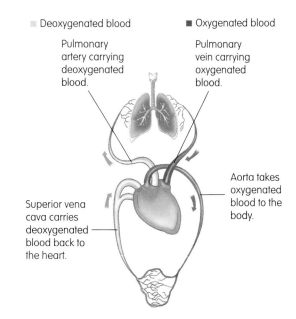

■ Deoxygenated blood   ■ Oxygenated blood

Pulmonary artery carrying deoxygenated blood.

Pulmonary vein carrying oxygenated blood.

Aorta takes oxygenated blood to the body.

Superior vena cava carries deoxygenated blood back to the heart.

Part of circulatory system	Pathway
1. Pulmonary artery	Takes deoxygenated blood out of the heart.
2.	
3.	
4.	
5.	
6. Aorta	Takes oxygenated blood away from the heart to the…
7.	
8.	
9.	
10. Right ventricle	Pumps blood out of the heart to the pulmonary artery.

1.2.2 A healthy, active lifestyle and your cardiovascular system   © Folens (copiable page)

Worksheet 2: The pathway of blood in the body

Level B   **Student's Book page 159**

Tasks

1 — Study the diagram. Track the pathway of blood in the body, starting at the heart leading into the pulmonary artery.

2 — Complete the table below by listing a part of the circulatory system and the pathway the blood takes, using statements from the statement bank. Three of the items have been completed to help you.

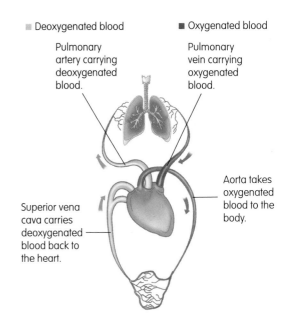

■ Deoxygenated blood   ■ Oxygenated blood

Pulmonary artery carrying deoxygenated blood.

Pulmonary vein carrying oxygenated blood.

Aorta takes oxygenated blood to the body.

Superior vena cava carries deoxygenated blood back to the heart.

Part of circulatory system	Pathway
1. Pulmonary artery	Takes deoxygenated blood out of the heart.
2.	
3.	
4.	
5.	
6. Aorta	Takes oxygenated blood away from the heart to the…
7.	
8.	
9.	
10. Right ventricle	Pumps blood out of the heart to the pulmonary artery.

Statement bank

- Left atrium – oxygenated blood pumped to the…
- Right atrium – pumps deoxygenated blood to the…
- Left ventricle – takes oxygenated blood out of the heart.
- Vena cava – takes deoxygenated blood back to the heart.
- Lungs – blood picks up oxygen and exits lungs via the…
- Pulmonary vein – takes oxygenated blood to the…
- Body – oxygen is used by working muscles and then to the…

Worksheet 3: Three types of blood vessels

Level A **Student's Book pages 156–157**

Tasks

1 — Complete the table below by giving information on the three types of blood vessels.

Artery	Capillary	Vein
	Walls are one cell thick	
		Takes blood to the heart
Mostly carries oxygenated blood		

2 — In your own words, state why the design of each blood vessel suits its purpose.

Artery: _____

_____

_____

_____

Capillary: _____

_____

_____

_____

Vein: _____

_____

_____

_____

1.2.2 A healthy, active lifestyle and your cardiovascular system   © Folens (copiable page)

Worksheet 3: Three types of blood vessels

Level B   **Student's Book pages 156–157**

Task

Complete the table below by giving information on the three types of blood vessels. Use the statements in the statement bank to help you. Each statement is used once.

> There are seven statements for both arteries and veins, but only six for capillaries.

Statement bank

- Fed by the arteries at one end
- Has thin walls
- Has a strong pulse
- Has a less elastic quality
- Walls are semi-permeable
- Has valves
- Minute internal diameter
- Takes blood away from the heart
- Feeds the veins at the other end
- Has no pulse
- Does not have valves
- Works under low pressure
- Does not have valves
- Carries deoxygenated blood
- Blood enters at a high pressure
- Has an elastic quality
- Has thick walls

Artery	Capillary	Vein
	Walls are one cell thick	
		Takes blood to the heart
Mostly carries oxygenated blood		

Worksheet 4: The composition of blood

Level A   Student's Book page 160

Tasks

1 — Link the two halves of each sentence together so that they make sense and form a true statement.

Red blood cells are called…
The main function of red blood cells…
In the red blood cells is haemoglobin; this helps…
White blood cells protect the body…
White blood cells are also called…
White blood cells are produced…
The platelets' job is…
Platelets are smaller parts…
Plasma is 90 per cent water and makes up…
Plasma contains plasma proteins that help…

…55 per cent of the volume of blood.
…is to transport oxygen.
…by going to the source of infection.
…the transportation of oxygen to the working muscles.
…erythrocytes.
…in both the long bones and the lymph tissue of the body.
…leukocytes.
…to clot the blood.
…the circulation between cells and tissue.
…of larger cells.

2 — Write two sentences about each of the following:
- haemoglobin
- fibrinogen.

_____

_____

_____

_____

_____

_____

_____

_____

_____

_____

_____

_____

Worksheet 4: The composition of blood

Level B   **Student's Book page 160**

Task

Link the two halves of each sentence together so that they make sense and form a true statement. Write each of them out in your workbook.

> Look again at your workbook notes to remind you of the ideas in the sentences.

Red blood cells are called…
The main function of red blood cells…
In the red blood cells is haemoglobin; this helps…
White blood cells protect the body…
White blood cells are also called…
White blood cells are produced…
The platelets' job is…
Platelets are smaller parts…
Plasma is 90 per cent water and makes up…
Plasma contains plasma proteins that help…

…55 per cent of the volume of blood.
…is to transport oxygen.
…by going to the source of infection.
…the transportation of oxygen to the working muscles.
…erythrocytes.
…in both the long bones and the lymph tissue of the body.
…leukocytes.
…to clot the blood.
…the circulation between cells and tissue.
…of larger cells.

Worksheet 5: Effects of exercise on the heart

Level A   **Student's Book pages 155–166**

Task

Complete the paragraphs below by filling in the gaps.

> When you have written each entry, read the whole sentence and check that it makes sense.

At rest, the heart beats about _____. This is called the _____.

This provides enough _____ to the muscles when they are not undertaking extra exercise. Every

heartbeat pumps blood out of the heart, this is called the _____. Over a minute, the total blood

pumped out of the heart is called the _____.

During exercise, the heart rate _____. The heart rate depends on the type of exercise. If it is easy, the

pulse goes up a little, if it is more intense then it rises further.

The maximum heart/pulse rate is calculated by the following formula: _____.

At rest, the stroke volume pumps about _____ of blood. During exercise, this could increase to 130ml,

depending on fitness levels.

To calculate the cardiac output multiply the _____. This gives the amount

of blood ejected from the heart per minute. As the heart rate and stroke volume increase with exercise, so the

cardiac output will increase as well. After exercise, the blood returns to its resting rate. The time it takes to do this is

called the _____. A cool-down can help the body gradually return to the resting heart rate. This

takes about five minutes depending on the fitness level and type of cool-down.

Worksheet 5: Effects of exercise on the heart

Level B   **Student's Book pages 155–166**

Task

Complete the paragraphs below by filling in the gaps. Use the statement bank to help you; they are used once only.

> When you have written each entry, read the whole sentence and check that it makes sense. Write the statements in pencil until you are sure they are correctly placed.

At rest, the heart beats about _____. This is called the _____.

This provides enough _____ to the muscles when they are not undertaking extra exercise. Every

heartbeat pumps blood out of the heart, this is called the _____. Over a minute, the total blood

pumped out of the heart is called the _____.

During exercise, the heart rate _____. The heart rate depends on the type of exercise. If it is easy, the

pulse goes up a little, if it is more intense then it rises further.

The maximum heart/pulse rate is calculated by the following formula: _____.

At rest, the stroke volume pumps about _____ of blood. During exercise, this could increase to 130ml,

depending on fitness levels.

To calculate the cardiac output multiply the _____. This gives the amount

of blood ejected from the heart per minute. As the heart rate and stroke volume increase with exercise, so the

cardiac output will increase as well. After exercise, the blood returns to its resting rate. The time it takes to do this is

called the _____. A cool-down can help the body gradually return to the resting heart rate. This

takes about five minutes depending on the fitness level and type of cool-down.

Statement bank

- increases
- cardiac output
- resting heart rate
- oxygen
- stroke volume

- recovery rate
- 85ml
- 220 – age
- 72 beats per minute
- stroke volume by the heart rate

Worksheet 6: Immediate effects of exercise on the performer

Level A **Student's Book pages 165–166**

Task

Look at the image below, which lists the effects that exercise has on the body. Fill in the gaps to complete the sentences.

a) The _____ reddens when blood vessels _____.

b) _____ volume increases.

c) The body _____ _____ to rid itself of waste products.

d) Red _____ take the oxygen to the working muscles.

e) Working _____ produce heat.

f) _____ widen to let more blood through.

g) The _____ increases.

h) _____, a waste product, is removed from the body and left on the surface of the skin.

i) Blood speeds up to help control the _____ to stop _____ exhaustion.

j) More_____ is required by the working muscles.

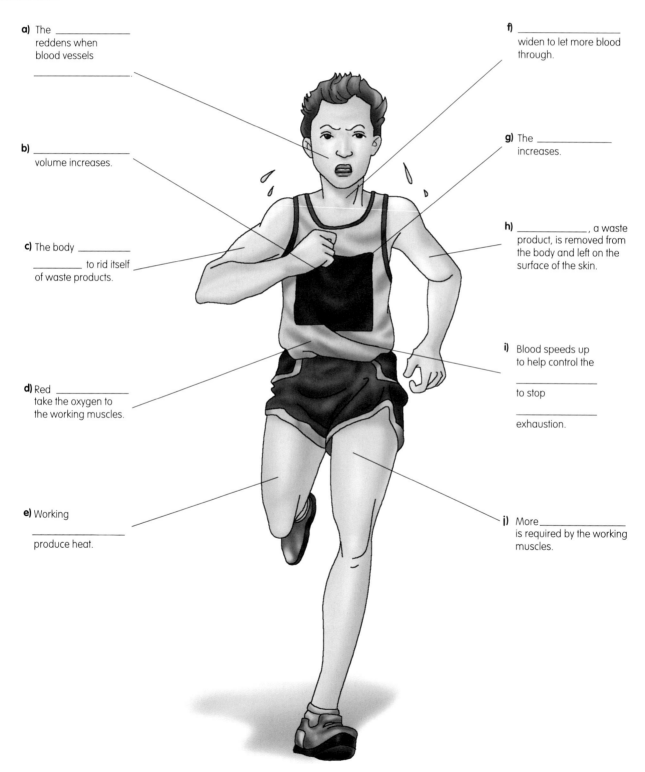

1.2.2 A healthy, active lifestyle and your cardiovascular system

Worksheet 6: Immediate effects of exercise on the performer

Level B　　　**Student's Book pages 165–166**

Task

Look at the diagram below, which lists the effects that exercise has on the body. Fill in the gaps to complete the sentences. Use the words from the word bank to help you.

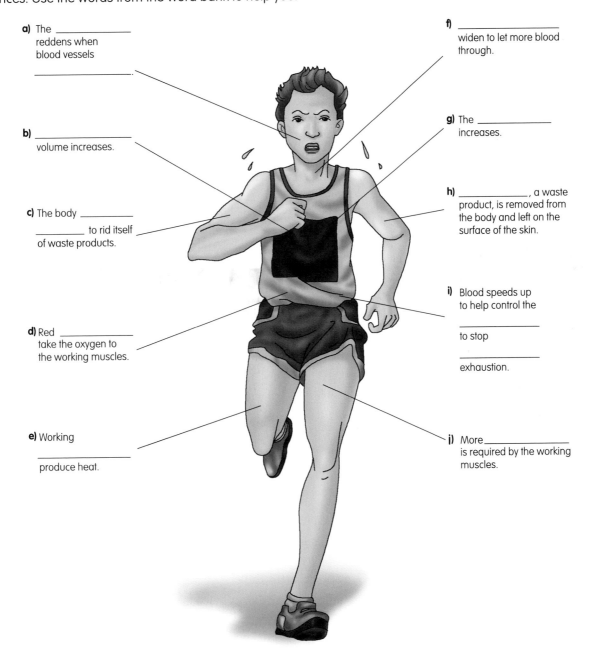

a) The _____ reddens when blood vessels _____.

b) _____ volume increases.

c) The body _____ _____ to rid itself of waste products.

d) Red _____ take the oxygen to the working muscles.

e) Working _____ produce heat.

f) _____ widen to let more blood through.

g) The _____ increases.

h) _____, a waste product, is removed from the body and left on the surface of the skin.

i) Blood speeds up to help control the _____ to stop _____ exhaustion.

j) More _____ is required by the working muscles.

Word bank

- temperature
- salt
- stroke
- sweats
- muscles
- oxygen
- heat
- heart rate
- dilate
- blood cells
- arteries
- face

　　1.2.2　A healthy, active lifestyle and your cardiovascular system

Homework 1: Interpreting a graph

Student's Book pages 157–158

Task

Study the graph below and answer the questions labelled a to h.

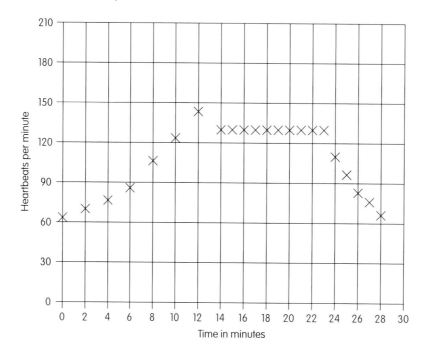

a) What is the highest pulse rate? _____

b) What is the lowest pulse rate?_____

c) What is the resting heart rate? _____

d) Is the activity aerobic or anaerobic? _____

e) At what stage is the athlete working hardest? _____

f) How many minutes into the activity is the athlete working hardest? _____

g) How can you tell that the activity reaches a stage where the degree of difficulty is the same? _____

h) For how long does this stage of consistent effort last? _____

1.2.2 A healthy, active lifestyle and your cardiovascular system

Homework 2: Questions on the circulatory system

Student's Book pages 155–166

Task

Read each of the following questions carefully and answer them with full sentences.

a) When is the best time to take your resting heart rate? _____

_____

_____

b) Why is this the best time? _____

_____

_____

c) Which type of blood do arteries carry? _____

_____

_____

d) What is the exception to this rule? _____

_____

_____

e) What happens to the heart rate during exercise? _____

_____

_____

f) Why do these changes happen? _____

_____

_____

g) Which blood vessels take blood from the heart? _____

h) Which blood cells have the job of carrying oxygen? _____

Extension 1: Effects of exercise on the heart

Student's Book pages 157–166

Tasks

1 — Simon has recently started exercising to improve his fitness. He has never studied Biology or GCSE PE and so has no understanding of how his body reacts to exercise. He has several questions he needs answering:

    1. "Why is my heart beating faster?"

    2. "I can feel my heart beating and I don't usually, why?"

    3. "Why does my face go red?"

    4. "After a while I start to perspire, what's that all about?"

    5. "When I lick my lips the perspiration is salty, why?"

    6. "When I stop exercising my heartbeat slows down, why?"

    7. "Why do I feel so hot?"

2 — Answer all of Simon's questions in the space provided.

1.2.2 A healthy, active lifestyle and your cardiovascular system

© Folens (copiable page)

Extension 2: Interpreting a graph 1

Student's Book pages 157–158

Tasks

1 — Study the graph below, which shows the changing heart rate in a training session.

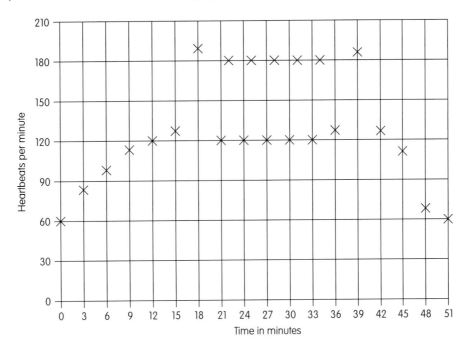

2 — Answer the following questions based on the graph above.

a) What is happening to the pulse between minutes:

i) 0–18? _____

_____

ii) 18–34? _____

_____

iii) 34–51? _____

_____

b) Why is the X at 18 higher? _____

_____

c) What kind of activity does the pulse pattern show? _____

_____

d) What training method is being used? _____

_____

e) Make a list of sportspeople that would use this method. _____

_____

Extension 3: Interpreting a graph 2

Student's Book pages 157–158

Tasks

1 — Study the graph below, which shows the changing heart rate in a training session.

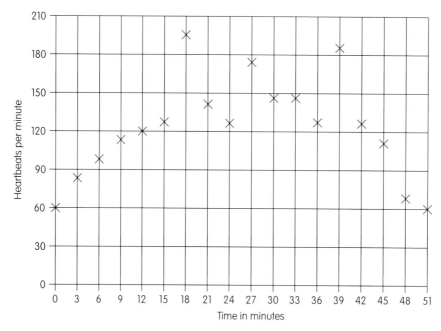

2 — Answer the following questions based on the graph above.

a) What is happening to the pulse between minutes:

i) 0–18? _____

_____

ii) 18–27? _____

_____

iii) 39? _____

_____

iv) 39–51? _____

_____

b) Why is the X at 18 minutes higher? _____

_____

c) What kind of activity does the pulse pattern show? _____

_____

d) What training method is being used? _____

_____

e) Make a list of sportspeople that would use this method. _____

The heart

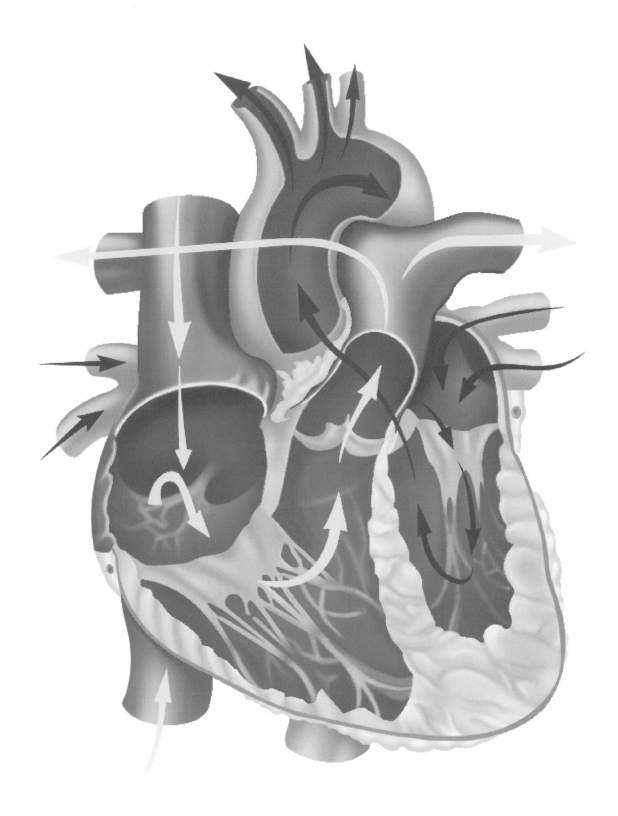

The heart and double circulatory system

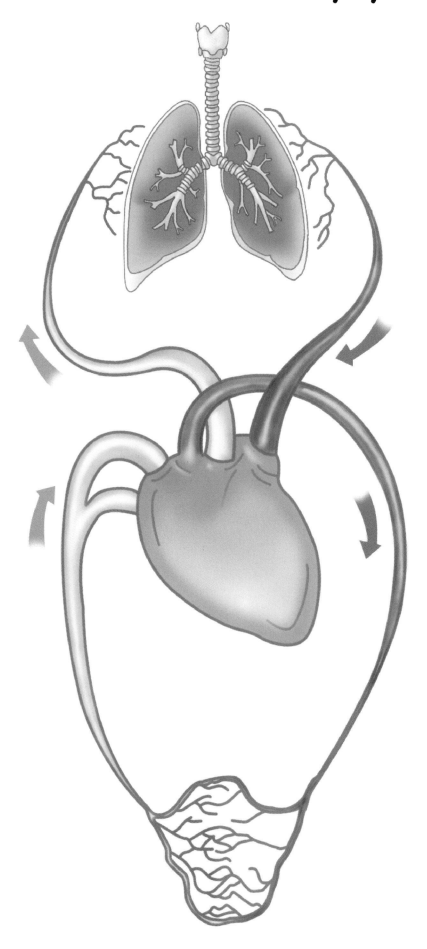

1.2.2 A healthy, active lifestyle and your cardiovascular system

© Folens (copiable page)

1.2 Your healthy, active body

1.2.3 A healthy, active lifestyle and your respiratory system

Contents

Worksheets

Homework sheets

Extension sheets

Blank diagrams for labelling

Worksheet 1: Air passages

Level A   **Student's Book pages 168–169**

Task

Name each part of the respiratory system pictured below and write a sentence about each one in your workbook.

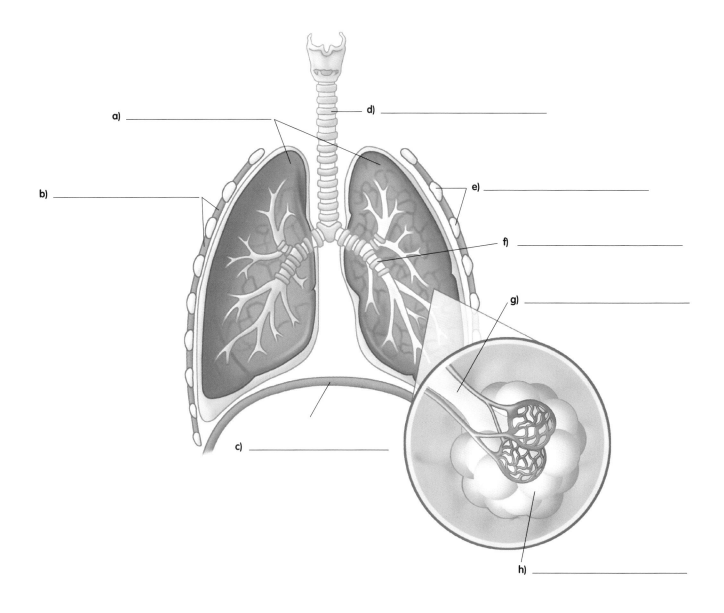

a) _____

b) _____

c) _____

d) _____

e) _____

f) _____

g) _____

h) _____

132   1.2.3 A healthy, active lifestyle and your respiratory system   © Folens (copiable page)

Worksheet 1: Air passages

Level B   **Student's Book pages 168–169**

Tasks

1 — Name each part of the respiratory system pictured below using the word bank to help you.

2 — Add a description of each part from the statements provided in the statement bank.

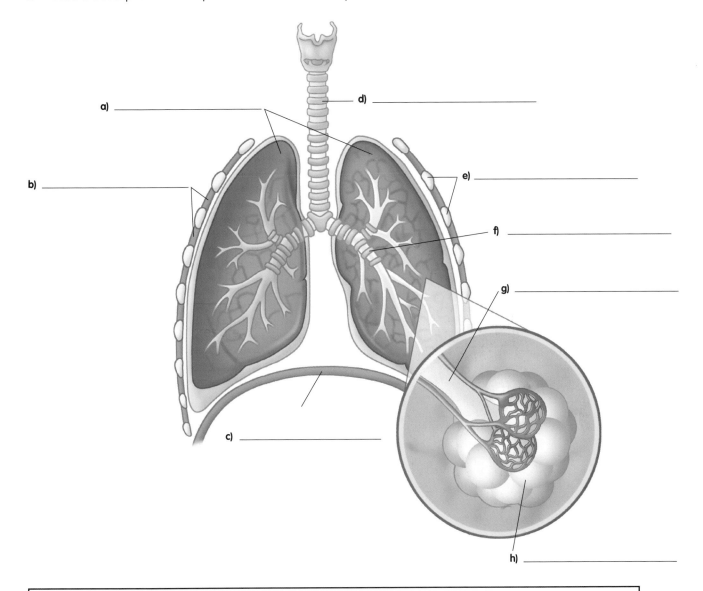

a) _____

d) _____

b) _____

e) _____

f) _____

g) _____

c) _____

h) _____

Word bank

- Trachea
- Bronchi
- Bronchioles
- Lungs
- Alveoli
- Diaphragm
- Intercostal muscles
- Ribs

Statement bank

- Muscles between the ribs that contract to enlarge the ribcage.
- Bones that form a cage to protect the organs in the chest area.
- Tube for the passage of air.
- One of two branches of the trachea.
- Smaller air tubes from the bronchi into the lungs.
- Major organs of respiration.
- Air sacs at the end of the bronchioles.
- Muscle that pulls down when breathing in.

Worksheet 2: Mechanism of breathing

Level A   **Student's Book page 170**

Tasks

1 — Study the following diagrams and information.

2 — In the spaces below write two paragraphs, one on inhalation and one on exhalation.

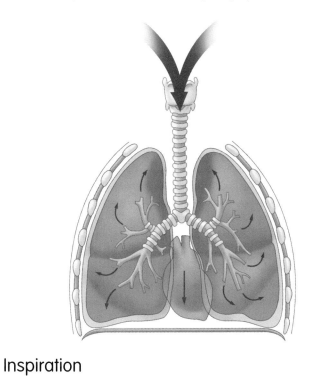

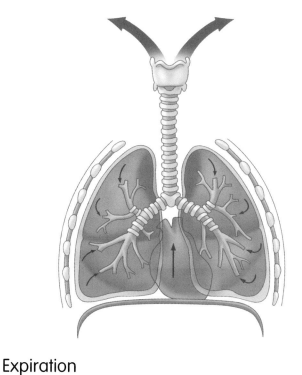

Inspiration   Expiration

_____   _____
_____   _____
_____   _____
_____   _____
_____   _____
_____   _____
_____   _____
_____   _____
_____   _____
_____   _____
_____   _____
_____   _____
_____   _____

1.2.3 A healthy, active lifestyle and your respiratory system   © Folens (copiable page)

Worksheet 2: Mechanism of breathing

Level B   **Student's Book page 170**

Tasks

Put the words from the word bank into the correct spaces below.

Words in bold are used twice.

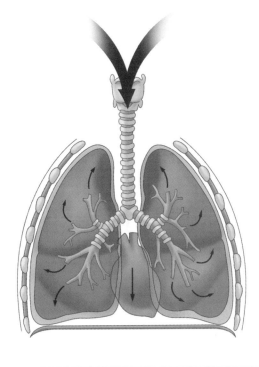

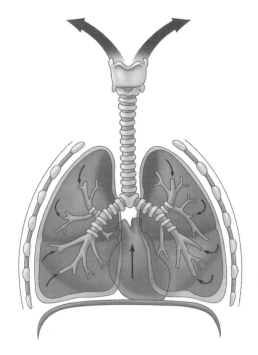

Word bank

- contract
- relaxes
- pulls down
- relax to dome shape
- pressure decreases

- pressure increases
- **diaphragm**
- **intercostal muscles**
- chest expands
- chest decreases

Inspiration

_____
_____
_____
_____
_____
_____
_____
_____

Expiration

_____
_____
_____
_____
_____
_____
_____
_____

Worksheet 3: Composition of inhaled and exhaled air

Level A **Student's Book page 174**

Tasks

1 — Study the partly completed table below about the composition of inhaled and exhaled air.

	Inhaled air	Exhaled air
		16%
	Trace	
Nitrogen		

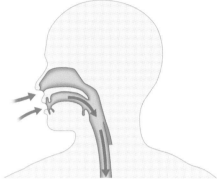

Inspiration

2 — Fill in the table using the word bank.

Word bank

- Oxygen
- Carbon dioxide
- 79%
- 79%
- 20%
- 4%

3 — Answer the following questions.

a) Why is there less oxygen in exhaled air?

_____

_____

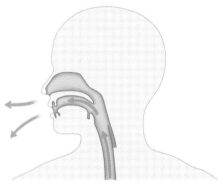

Expiration

b) Why is there an increased level of carbon dioxide in exhaled air?

_____

_____

4 — John has trained for 12 weeks for his long-distance event. How has this training helped improve his respiratory system?

_____

_____

_____

_____

_____

1.2.3 A healthy, active lifestyle and your respiratory system   © Folens (copiable page)

Worksheet 3: Composition of inhaled and exhaled air

Level B   Student's Book page 174

Tasks

1 — Study the partly completed table below about the composition of inhaled and exhaled air.

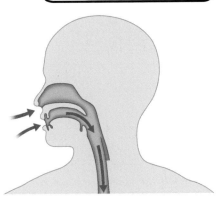

Use your workbook to help.

	Inhaled air	Exhaled air
		16%
	Trace	
Nitrogen		

Inspiration

2 — Fill in the table using the word bank.

Word bank

- Oxygen
- Carbon dioxide
- 79%
- 79%
- 20%
- 4%

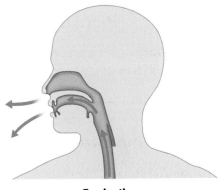

3 — Answer the following questions.

a) Why is there less oxygen in exhaled air?

_____

_____

Expiration

b) Why is there an increased level of carbon dioxide in exhaled air?

_____

_____

Worksheet 4: Anaerobic respiration

Level A   **Student's Book pages 171–172**

Tasks

1 — Look at the table below, which describes the changes in respiration of an athlete taking part in a sprint race.

Order of events	Letter	Sentence
1	f	She breathes slowly and respires aerobically.
2		
3		
4		
5		
6		
7	f	She breathes slowly and respires aerobically.

2 — Write the sentences from below in the table in the correct order. Two have been done to help you.

    a) She breathes quickly and respires aerobically.

    b) The oxygen debt is repaid.

    c) Her muscles ache.

    d) Lactic acid forms in the muscles.

    e) She begins anaerobic respiration in her muscles.

    f) She breathes slowly and respires aerobically.

3 — Sarah is a heptathlete. List the six events (out of seven) that rely on anaerobic respiration.

_____

_____

_____

_____

_____

_____

_____

4 — Make a list of features that help identify anaerobic activities.

_____

_____

_____

_____

_____

_____

_____

1.2.3 A healthy, active lifestyle and your respiratory system   © Folens (copiable page)

Worksheet 4: Anaerobic respiration

Level B **Student's Book pages 171–172**

Tasks

1 — Look at the table below, which describes the changes in respiration of an athlete taking part in a sprint race.

Order of events	Letter	Sentence
1	f	She breathes slowly and respires aerobically.
2		
3		
4		
5		
6		
7	f	She breathes slowly and respires aerobically.

2 — Write the sentences below in the table in the correct order. Two have been done to help you.

    a) She breathes quickly and respires aerobically.

    b) The oxygen debt is repaid.

    c) Her muscles ache.

    d) Lactic acid forms in the muscles.

    e) She begins anaerobic respiration in her muscles.

    f) She breathes slowly and respires aerobically.

Worksheet 5: Changes in the athlete during exercise

Level A   **Student's Book pages 169–175**

Tasks

Many changes happen to an athlete as they exercise. This worksheet looks at the effects on the respiratory and circulatory systems.

1— Study the diagram of the athlete below and label each arrowed part of the athlete's body.

2— For each labelled area, write a change that happens to that part during exercise.

a) _____

c) _____

e) _____

b) _____

d) _____

f) _____

3— Write down what happens to each of the following during exercise:

    a) Tidal volume: _____

    b) Residual volume: _____

    c) Vital capacity: _____

    d) Forced breathing: _____

Worksheet 5: Changes in the athlete during exercise

Level B   **Student's Book pages 169–175**

Task

Many changes happen to an athlete as they exercise. This worksheet looks at the effects on the respiratory and circulatory systems.

1 — Study the diagram of the athlete below and label each arrowed part of the athlete's body.

2 — For each labelled area, write a change that happens to that part during exercise.

> These changes are listed in statement bank 1 below.

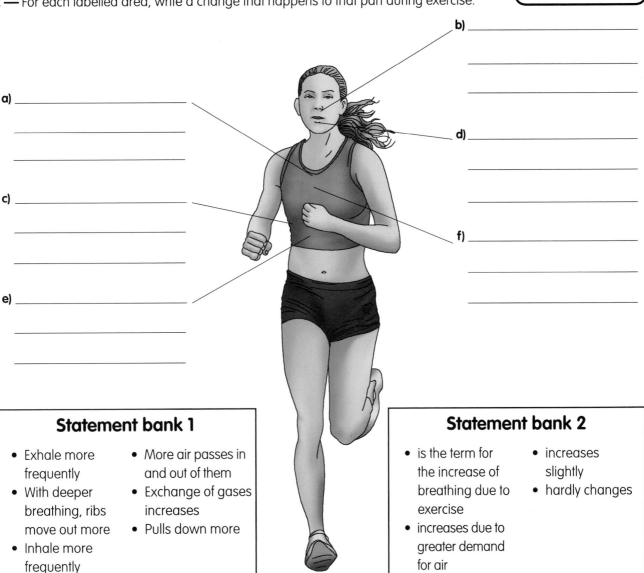

a) _____

_____

_____

c) _____

_____

_____

e) _____

_____

_____

b) _____

_____

_____

d) _____

_____

f) _____

_____

_____

Statement bank 1

- Exhale more frequently
- With deeper breathing, ribs move out more
- Inhale more frequently
- More air passes in and out of them
- Exchange of gases increases
- Pulls down more

Statement bank 2

- is the term for the increase of breathing due to exercise
- increases due to greater demand for air
- increases slightly
- hardly changes

3 — Link the correct statements from statement bank 2 to the names of the different lung capacities and types of breathing when affected by exercise.

a) Tidal volume: _____

b) Residual volume: _____

c) Vital capacity: _____

d) Forced breathing: _____

Homework 1: How breathing works

Student's Book page 170

Task

Carefully read the beginnings and ends of sentences below. Link the correct parts together to make sentences about the mechanism of breathing and write them out in the space provided.

Beginnings
a) By breathing through my nose,…
b) The air goes into my trachea,…
c) At the end of the bronchi are…
d) Around the lungs is…
e) When breathing in,…
f) The ribcage becomes bigger due to…
g) As the ribcage gets bigger,…
h) Air is pushed out of the lungs…

Endings
1) …the pleural membrane.
2) …which is a tube with rings of cartilage.
3) …the lungs are pulled out and air is sucked in.
4) …the diaphragm flattens and pulls down.
5) …when the intercostal muscles relax and the ribcage gets smaller.
6) …smaller tubes called bronchioles.
7) …the air is warmed and filtered of fine dust.
8) …the intercostal muscles contracting.

1.2.3 A healthy, active lifestyle and your respiratory system

Homework 2: Aerobic and anaerobic respiration

Student's Book pages 171–172

Task

Read the brief account below of what happened to a runner when he tried to change the pace in his 20 minute run. Answer the questions on what happened to him.

A long-distance runner starts their run after their warm-up.
They run for 20 minutes.
Their pace is at a moderate level.
The temperature is quite high as it is a hot day.
After running steadily for two miles, they try to increase their pace.
As a result, their leg muscles begin to hurt and they have to return to their previous pace.

a) How deep would the runner's breathing be when they were working moderately for a prolonged period of time?

_____

_____

_____

b) Why would the heart beat faster?

_____

_____

_____

c) Why would the runner start to sweat?

_____

_____

_____

d) Why did their legs begin to hurt after the increase of pace?

_____

_____

_____

e) Say why, if they had sprinted for longer at the beginning of the race, they would have had to drop back soon after the start.

_____

_____

_____

Homework 3: Aerobic and anaerobic respiration in various sports

Student's Book pages 171–172

Tasks

1 — Study the list below of different types of physical activity. Decide whether the activity uses more aerobic or anaerobic respiration. Write AE for aerobic and AN for anaerobic in the boxes provided.

a) Squash ☐

b) Football ☐

c) 200m running ☐

d) Basketball ☐

e) Long-distance swimming ☐

f) Javelin throwing ☐

g) Long jumping ☐

h) Long-distance cycling ☐

i) Tennis ☐

j) Netball ☐

2 — Make a list below of aerobic actions and anaerobic actions within a game of your choice.

Chosen sport:

_____

Aerobic actions:

_____

_____

_____

_____

_____

_____

Anaerobic actions:

_____

_____

_____

_____

_____

_____

_____

1.2.3 A healthy, active lifestyle and your respiratory system

Extension 1: Aerobic and anaerobic training

Student's Book pages 171–172

Tasks

1 — List five sports and say whether participants would train aerobically or anaerobically or a mixture of both to improve their performance.

Sport 1: _____

Sport 2: _____

Sport 3: _____

Sport 4: _____

Sport 5: _____

2 — Rebecca trains both aerobically and anaerobically. Decide on a sport for Rebecca that would include a mix of both types of respiration and detail what activities and exercises might be included in her training session. State clearly the aerobic and anaerobic phases of the session.

> Draw on your own experiences to help your answer.

_____

_____

_____

_____

_____

_____

_____

_____

_____

_____

_____

_____

_____

_____

_____

_____

_____

_____

_____

_____

Extension 2: Exercise and the respiratory system

Student's Book pages 177–178

Task

Abi finished her warm-up and began vigorous exercise. She noticed several changes to her body and understood what was happening.

Write what you think Abi understood to be happening to the following:

a) Breathing and breathing rate

_____

_____

_____

_____

b) VO_2

_____

_____

_____

_____

c) Oxygen debt

_____

_____

_____

_____

d) Vital capacity

_____

_____

_____

_____

e) Residual volume

_____

_____

_____

_____

Extension 3: Long-term effects of training

Student's Book pages 171–172

Tasks

1 — Training aerobically and training anaerobically have different long-term effects on the respiratory system. Write what you know about their effects on the respiratory system.

_____

_____

_____

_____

_____

_____

_____

_____

_____

_____

_____

_____

2 — Choose one sport that would benefit from aerobic training and detail what activities and exercises might be included in a training session.

> Draw on your own experiences in training to help your answer.

_____

_____

_____

_____

_____

_____

_____

_____

_____

_____

_____

Parts of the respiratory system

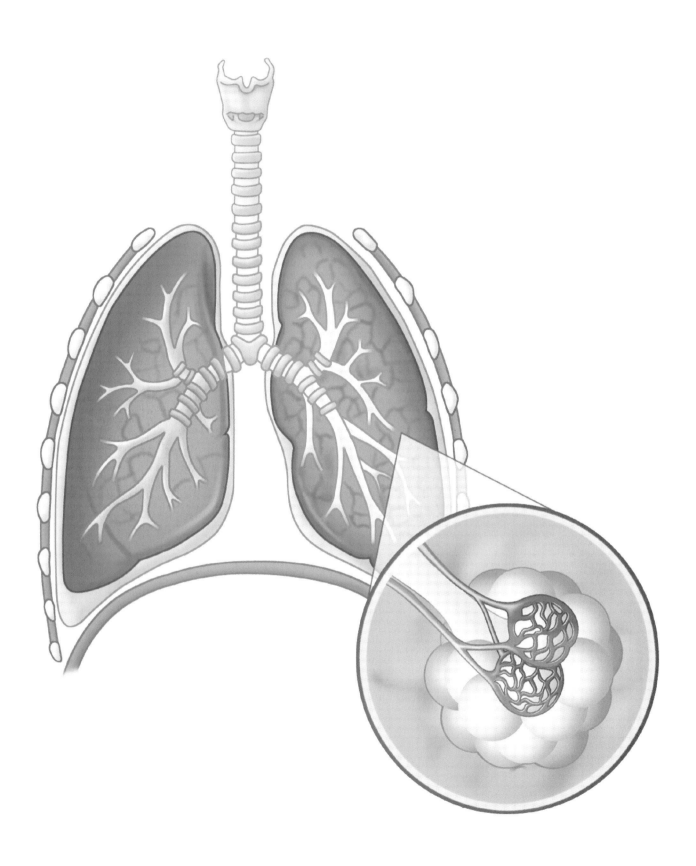

1.2.3 A healthy, active lifestyle and your respiratory system

The alveoli

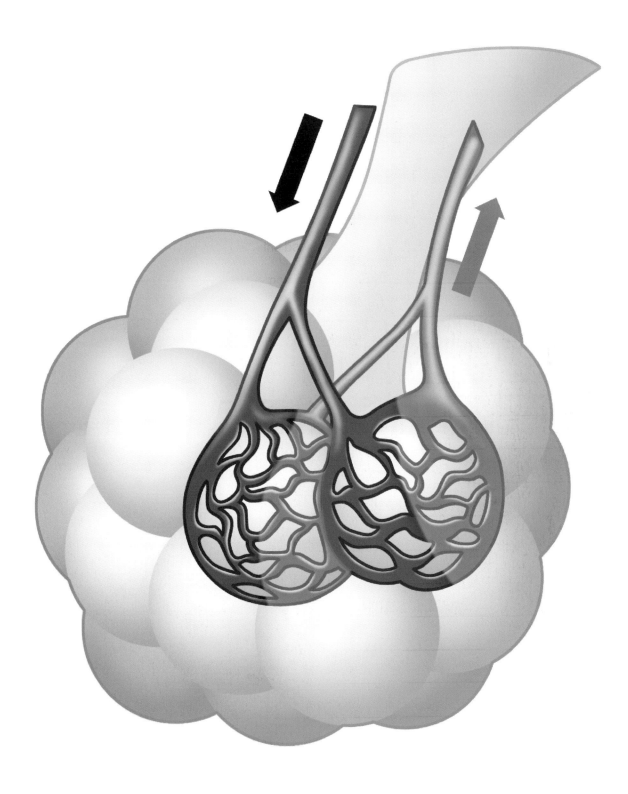

Inspiration and expiration

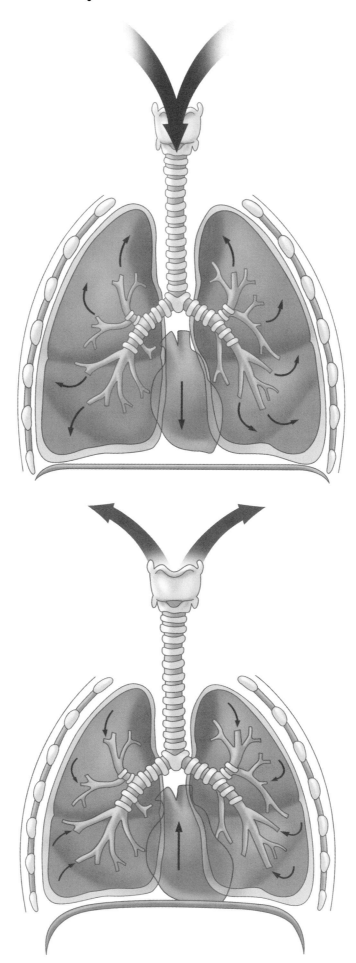

1.2.3 A healthy, active lifestyle and your respiratory system

1.2 Your healthy, active body

1.2.4 A healthy, active lifestyle and your muscular system

Contents

Worksheets

Homework sheets

Extension sheets

Blank diagrams for labelling

Worksheet 1: Types of muscle

Level A   **Student's Book page 182**

Tasks

1 — Study the table below and put each of the words from the word bank under the correct heading. The word in bold is used twice.

Voluntary	Involuntary	Cardiac
_____ _____ _____ _____ _____	_____ _____ _____ _____ _____	_____ _____ _____ _____ _____

Word bank

- heart
- most common
- blood vessels
- striated

- smooth
- **automatic**
- involuntary

- never rests
- intestines
- consciously controlled

2 — Write four sentences on how the following help the sportsperson:

a) Cardiac muscle

_____

_____

_____

_____

b) Voluntary muscle

_____

_____

_____

_____

_____

Worksheet 1: Types of muscle

Level B   **Student's Book page 182**

Task

Study the table below and put each of the words from the word bank under the correct heading. The word in bold is used twice.

The initials of each word have been given to help you.

Voluntary	Involuntary	Cardiac
s_____	s_____	h_____
c_____ c_____	a_____	i_____
m_____ c_____	i_____	a_____
	b_____ v_____	n_____ r_____

Word bank

- heart
- most common
- blood vessels
- striated
- smooth

- **automatic**
- involuntary
- never rests
- intestines
- consciously controlled

Worksheet 2: Linking muscles to a sport

Level A   **Student's Book pages 180–188**

Tasks

1 — Study the sporting action photos below.

2 — Next to each photo, describe the action and give the name of the main muscles being used. The muscles are listed in the word bank to help you. Each word can be used more than once.

a) _____

_____

_____

_____

_____

b) _____

_____

_____

_____

_____

c) _____

_____

_____

_____

_____

Word bank

- biceps
- triceps
- deltoids
- pectorals

- trapezius
- abdominals
- latissimus dorsi
- gluteals

- quadriceps
- hamstrings
- gastrocnemius

1.2.4 A healthy, active lifestyle and your muscular system

© Folens (copiable page)

Worksheet 2: Linking muscles to a sport

Level B **Student's Book pages 180–188**

Tasks

1 — Study the sporting action photos below.

2 — Under each photo, describe the action and give the name of the main muscles being used. The muscles are listed in individual word banks to help you. Each word can be used more than once.

a) _____

_____

_____

_____

_____

Word bank

- biceps
- pectorals
- triceps
- trapezius
- deltoids
- latissimus dorsi

b) _____

_____

_____

_____

_____

Word bank

- abdominals
- hamstrings
- quadriceps
- gluteals

c) _____

_____

_____

_____

_____

Word bank

- abdominals
- hamstrings
- gluteals
- gastrocnemius
- quadriceps

Worksheet 3: Diagram of the arm

Level A **Student's Book page 186**

Tasks

1 — Label all of the parts of the arm diagram below.

a) _____

b) _____

c) _____

d) _____

e) _____

f) _____

g) _____

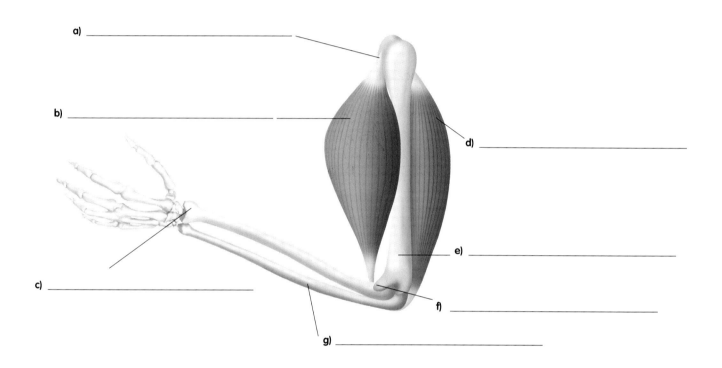

2 — Colour in the origin and insertion.

© Folens (copiable page)

Worksheet 3: Diagram of the arm

Level B **Student's Book page 186**

Tasks

1 — Label all of the parts of the arm diagram below. The first letter of the word is given in each case.

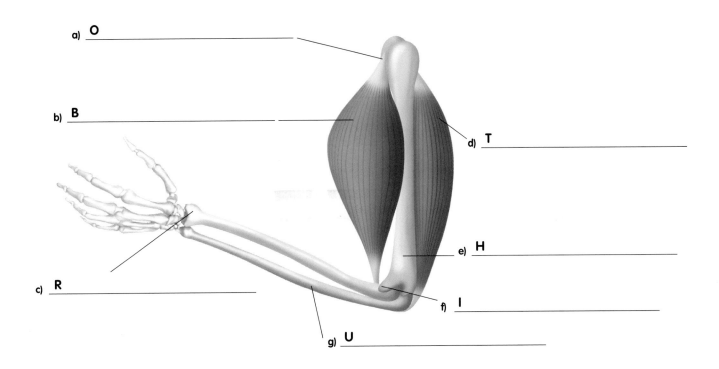

a) O _____

b) B _____

d) T _____

c) R _____

e) H _____

f) I _____

g) U _____

2 — Colour in the origin and insertion.

Worksheet 4: Diagram of the leg

Level A **Student's Book page 187**

Tasks

1 — Study the diagram of the leg and its muscles.

2 — Label the diagram, using the words from the word bank.

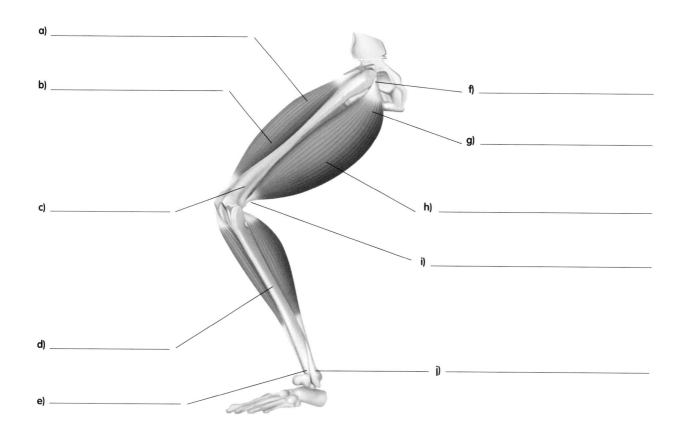

a) _____

b) _____

c) _____

d) _____

e) _____

f) _____

g) _____

h) _____

i) _____

j) _____

Word bank		
• Femur	• Flexor	• Origin
• Tibia	• Fibula	• Tendon
• Hamstring	• Extensor	• Insertion tendon
• Quadriceps		

3 — Read the paragraph 'How muscles work in pairs' on page 187 of the Student's Book. From the information given, add an arrow to the prime mover and another to the antagonist on the diagram.

1.2.4 A healthy, active lifestyle and your muscular system

Worksheet 4: Diagram of the leg

Level B   **Student's Book page 187**

Tasks

1 — Study the diagram of the leg and its muscles.

2 — Label the diagram, using the words from the word bank. The first letter of each part has been given to help you.

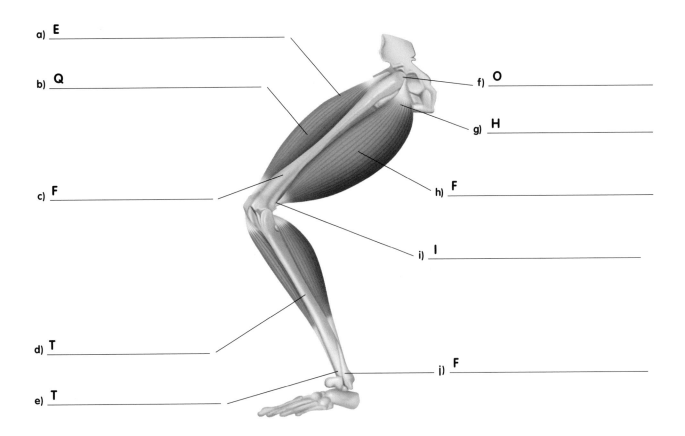

a) **E** _____

b) **Q** _____

c) **F** _____

d) **T** _____

e) **T** _____

f) **O** _____

g) **H** _____

h) **F** _____

i) **I** _____

j) **F** _____

Word bank

- Femur
- Tibia
- Hamstring
- Quadriceps
- Flexor
- Fibula
- Extensor
- Origin
- Tendon
- Insertion tendon

---

3 — Read the paragraph 'How muscles work in pairs' on page 187 of the Student's Book. From the information given, add an arrow to the prime mover and another to the antagonist on the diagram.

Worksheet 5: Sport links and twitch muscle fibres

Level A **Student's Book pages 184–185**

Tasks

1 — There are two columns in the table below, headed FTMF (fast twitch muscle fibres) and STMF (slow twitch muscle fibres). Read the statements in the statement bank and write each of them out again under the correct heading in the table.

Fast twitch	Slow twitch

Statement bank

- Contract fast, producing a powerful action
- Stay efficient over long periods
- Produce short bursts of energy
- Tire quickly
- Suit sprinting and throwing events
- Have a very good oxygen supply
- Best for events that take a long time to complete, such as long-distance running, swimming and cycling
- Suited to slow, prolonged activity

2 — Choose two sports, one relying on fast twitch muscle fibres, the other on slow twitch muscle fibres. Then describe the actions using the different twitch fibres.

_____

_____

_____

_____

_____

_____

_____

_____

1.2.4 A healthy, active lifestyle and your muscular system   © Folens (copiable page)

Worksheet 5: Sport links and twitch muscle fibres

Level B   **Student's Book pages 184–185**

Task

There are two columns in the table below, headed FTMF (fast twitch muscle fibres) and STMF (slow twitch muscle fibres). Read the statements in the statement bank and write each of them out again under the correct heading in the table.

Fast twitch	Slow twitch

Statement bank

- Contract fast, producing a powerful action
- Stay efficient over long periods
- Produce short bursts of energy
- Tire quickly
- Suit sprinting and throwing events
- Have a very good oxygen supply
- Best for events that take a long time to complete, such as long-distance running, swimming and cycling
- Suited to slow, prolonged activity

Homework 1: Functions of the muscles

Student's Book page 180

Task

Describe the function of the following muscles and link a sporting action to each of them.

Use your workbook to help you.
Look at the location of the muscles.
Link them with a type of movement.

a) Gastrocnemius

_____

_____

_____

_____

_____

b) Deltoids

_____

_____

_____

_____

_____

_____

c) Latissimus dorsi

_____

_____

_____

_____

_____

_____

d) Gluteals

_____

_____

_____

_____

_____

_____

_____

1.2.4 A healthy, active lifestyle and your muscular system

© Folens (copiable page)

Homework 2: Muscles of the body

Student's Book page 180

Tasks

1 — Label the diagram of the body with the appropriate muscles.

a) _____

b) _____

c) _____

d) _____

e) _____

f) _____

g) _____

h) _____

i) _____

j) _____

k) _____

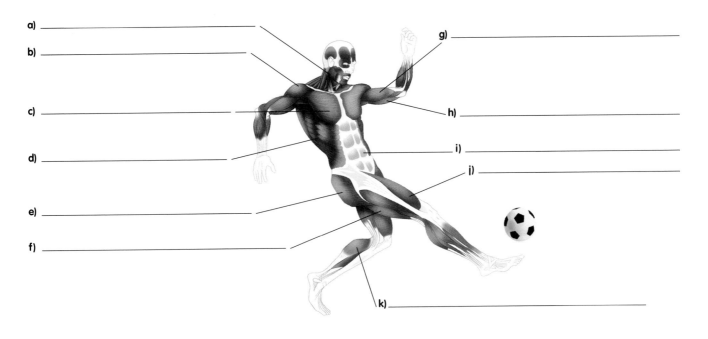

2 — a) Give two examples of muscles working in pairs.

_____

_____

_____

_____

b) Explain how these muscles work in pairs.

_____

_____

_____

_____

_____

_____

_____

_____

_____

_____

_____

_____

_____

Homework 3: Multiple-choice questions

Student's Book pages 180–188

Tasks

1 — Read the questions below and choose the correct answer from those given. Read the question again to make sure and then write the correct letter in the space provided.

1. Muscles work antagonistically. When the knee joint bends back the:

   a) Quadriceps are the flexor and prime mover

   b) Hamstrings are the extensor and antagonist

   c) Gastrocnemius is the flexor and antagonist

   d) Hamstrings are the flexor and prime mover

2. Which of the following best describes cardiac muscle?

   a) Never tires, is involuntary, only found in the heart

   b) Involuntary, smooth, found mainly in the heart

   c) Greatest amount of muscle in the body, never tires, voluntary

   d) Smooth, involuntary, found in the heart

3. The following can be said of fast twitch muscle fibres:

   a) Quick release of energy, good oxygen supply, can work for long periods of time

   b) Slow release of energy, fairly good oxygen supply, suited to explosive athletic events

   c) Suited to endurance events, slow release of energy, can work for long periods of time

   d) Suited to explosive athletic events, quick release of energy, produce powerful actions

4. Which of the following describes muscular strength?

   a) The ability of the muscle to hypertrophy

   b) The ability of the muscle to keep working for long periods of time

   c) The ability of the muscle to lift a maximum weight in one go

   d) The ability of the muscle to work without tiring

2 — Write out two multiple-choice questions of your own about muscles on the back of this sheet. Use the same method of asking questions as above. Refer to your workbook to help you.

1.2.4 A healthy, active lifestyle and your muscular system

Extension 1: Posture

Student's Book pages 183–184

Tasks

1 — Look carefully at the pictures below showing two different postures. Write a description of what you see next to each one. Comment about the head, shoulder, stomach and hip positions. Use the word bank to help you.

Word bank			
• in line	• shoulders	• spine	• curve
• hips	• round shoulders	• drooping head	

2 — Copy and complete the following concept map into your workbook on good posture.

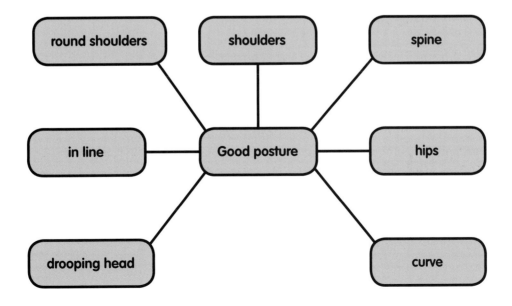

Extension 2: Fast and slow twitch muscle fibres

Student's Book pages 184–185

Tasks

1 — Divide the words listed in the statement bank into two groups – one for fast twitch muscle fibres the other for slow twitch muscle fibres – and write them out in the spaces provided.

Fast twitch muscle fibres

1. _____

2. _____

3. _____

4. _____

5. _____

6. _____

Slow twitch muscle fibres

1. _____

2. _____

3. _____

4. _____

5. _____

6. _____

7. _____

8. _____

Statement bank

- Contractions are fast
- Use myglobin/mitochondria
- Tire quickly
- Used for speed/explosive events
- White in colour
- Can repeat many times
- Used for endurance events
- Not as good supply of oxygen as STMF
- Fast, powerful action
- Good oxygen supply
- Gets energy by using oxygen
- Contractions are slow
- Can work over prolonged periods
- Dark red in colour

---

2 — In sentences, write six facts about fast and slow twitch muscle fibres.

_____

_____

_____

_____

_____

_____

_____

_____

_____

_____

_____

_____

Extension 3: Questions requiring short answers

Student's Book pages 182–188

Tasks

1— Read the following statements carefully and fill in the gaps with the most appropriate answer.

a) Muscles can only _____.

b) When muscles work they contract. This makes them _____.

c) Muscles are attached to bone by _____.

d) The tendon that attaches the muscle to the bone where there is no movement is called _____.

e) The tendon that attaches the muscle to the bone where there is movement is called _____.

f) When muscles work as a pair to create movement, they work as _____ pairs of muscles.

g) The muscle that contracts, causing the movement, is called the _____.

h) The muscle that relaxes to cause least resistance to the contracting muscle is called _____.

i) Fast twitch muscle fibres are at work in the following sports: _____

_____

j) Slow twitch muscle fibres are at work in the following activities: _____

_____

k) Four facts about fast twitch muscle fibres are: _____

_____

_____

_____

_____

l) Four facts about slow twitch muscle fibres are: _____

_____

_____

_____

_____

m) Muscle tone is: _____

_____

n) Good posture helps with: _____

_____

Muscles of the body

1.2.4 A healthy, active lifestyle and your muscular system

Muscles of the arm

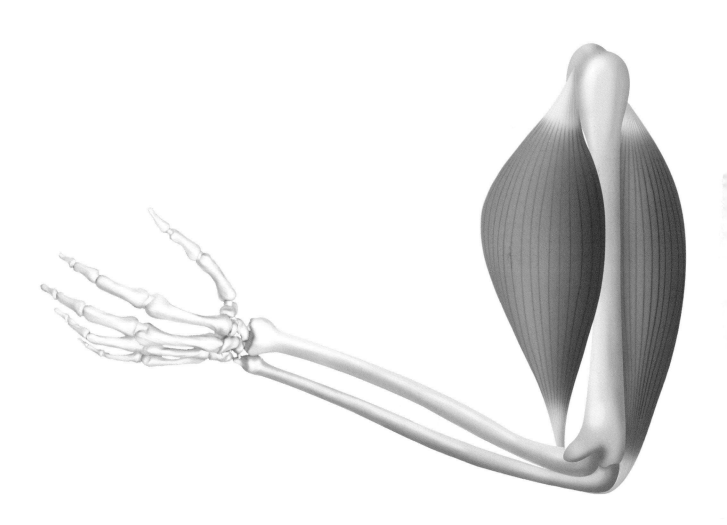

1.2.4 A healthy, active lifestyle and your muscular system

Muscles of the leg

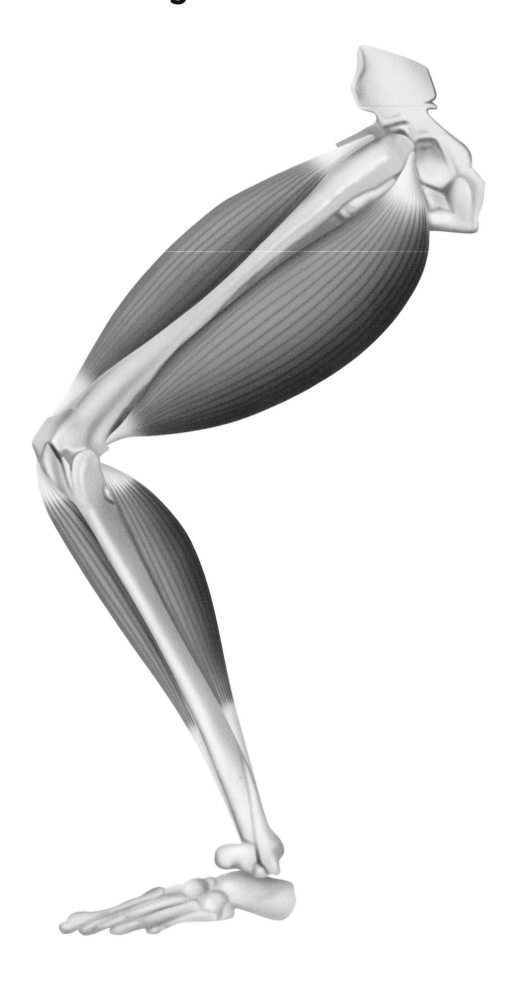

1.2.4 A healthy, active lifestyle and your muscular system

1.2 Your healthy, active body

1.2.5 A healthy, active lifestyle and your skeletal system

Contents

Bones

Worksheets

Homework sheets

Extension sheets

Joints

Worksheets

Homework sheets

Extension sheets

Blank diagrams for labelling

Worksheet 1: Protecting bones

Level A   Student's Book pages 198–201

Tasks

1 — At the top of each box below is the name of a protective bone. Add to each box the organs that each bone protects. Use the words from the word bank to help you.

> Think of where the organs are in your body and link them with the nearest protective bone.

Cranium

Ribs

Pelvic girdle

Vertebral column

Word bank

- spinal chord
- bladder
- liver
- lungs
- female reproductive organs
- brain
- heart
- spleen

2 — For each protective bone, give a sporting example of when it would come into use.

> For example: ribs – chesting down a ball in football.

_____

_____

_____

_____

_____

_____

_____

_____

Worksheet 1: Protecting bones

Level B   **Student's Book pages 198–201**

Task

At the top of each box below is the name of a protective bone. Add to each box the organs that each bone protects. Use the words from the word bank to help you.

> Think of where the organs are in your body and link them with the nearest protective bone.

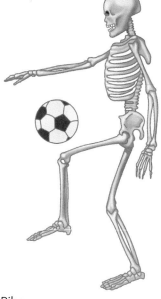

Cranium

Ribs

Pelvic girdle

Vertebral column

Word bank

- spinal chord
- bladder
- liver
- lungs
- female reproductive organs
- brain
- heart
- spleen

1.2.5 A healthy, active lifestyle and your skeletal system

Worksheet 2: Functions of the skeleton

Level A   **Student's Book pages 210–211**

Task

Insert the correct words to complete the sentences on the
functions of the skeleton below. Rewrite the complete sentences
in your workbook.

Rewriting the sentences in your
workbook will help you to remember
the information for use at a later date.

a) Some people choose a particular sport because of their _____ due to their skeleton size.

b) The skeleton provides the _____ on which the muscles hang.

c) We need our skeleton to work with the muscles to allow different _____.

d) When a player heads a ball their brain is _____ by part of their skeleton called the cranium.

e) Red blood cells are frequently being _____ in the long bones of the skeleton.

Worksheet 2: Functions of the skeleton

Level B   **Student's Book pages 210–211**

Task

Insert the correct words to complete the sentences on the functions of the skeleton below. Use words from the word bank. More words are provided than you need, so you will have to choose carefully.

> Rewriting the sentences in your workbook will help you to remember the information for use at a later date.

Rewrite the complete sentences in your workbook.

a) Some people choose a particular sport because of their _____ due to their skeleton size.

b) The skeleton provides the _____ on which the muscles hang.

c) We need our skeleton to work with the muscles to allow different _____.

d) When a player heads a ball their brain is _____ by part of their skeleton called the cranium.

e) Red blood cells are frequently being _____ in the long bones of the skeleton.

Word bank

- white blood cells
- shape
- muscles
- movements
- protected
- long bones
- holding bay
- skeleton
- produced
- elements
- support

1.2.5 A healthy, active lifestyle and your skeletal system

Worksheet 3: Grouping and classifying bones

Level A   **Student's Book pages 199–200**

Tasks

1 — Study the diagram of a skeleton below.

2 — Colour in the bones, according to their classification. Use a different colour for long, short, flat and irregular bones.

3 — Fill the colours in on the key with one colour for each class of bone used in question 2.

4 — Label the skeleton with the names of the bones.

> Use the groupings and the labelled diagram of a skeleton in the Student's Book to help you.

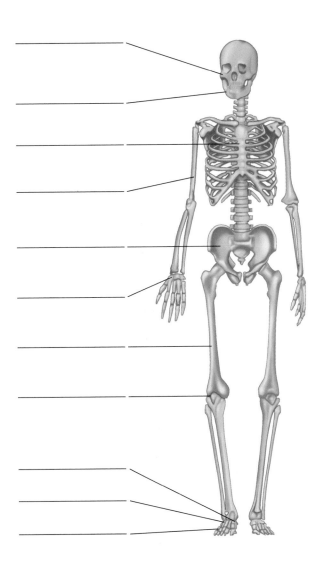
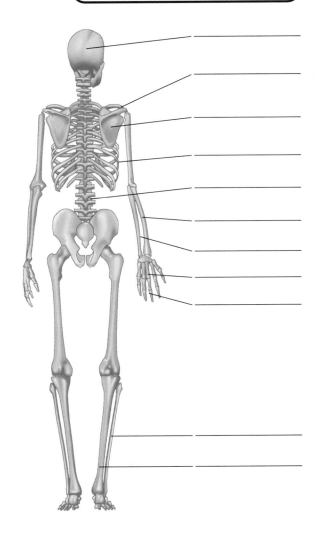

Key:
☐ Long bones
☐ Short bones
☐ Flat bones
☐ Irregular bones

Worksheet 3: Grouping and classifying bones

Level B   **Student's Book pages 199–200**

Tasks

1 — Study the diagram of a skeleton below.

2 — Colour in the bones, according to their classification. Use a different colour for long, short, flat and irregular bones.

3 — Fill the colours in on the key with one colour for each class of bone used in question 2.

4 — Label the skeleton with the names of the bones. The first initial of each bone has been given to help you.

> Use the groupings and the labelled diagram of a skeleton in the Student's Book to help you.

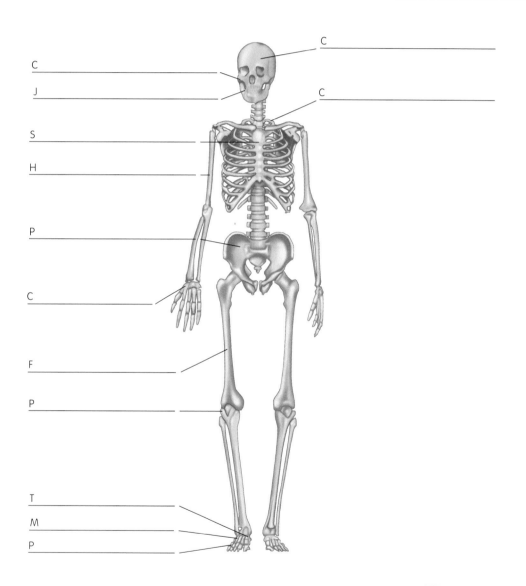

C

C
J
S
H
P
C
F
P
T
M
P

Key:

☐ Long bones
☐ Short bones
☐ Flat bones
☐ Irregular bones

1.2.5 A healthy, active lifestyle and your skeletal system   © Folens (copiable page)

Worksheet 4: Bones that link with sporting actions

Level A **Student's Book pages 196–211**

Tasks

1 — Study the photos below, of people taking part in different sports, and decide which bones they are using in the particular action they are performing.

2 — Write your answers in the spaces provided.

> Think of the action. For example, is it throwing, which involves the arms, or is it making a landing, and if so, using which part of the body? When you have worked out which part of the body is performing the main task, think of the bones in that region of the body.

a)

b)

c)

d)

Worksheet 4: Bones that link with sporting actions

Level B **Student's Book pages 196–211**

Tasks

1 — Study the photos below, of people taking part in different sports, and decide which bones the people are using in the particular action they are performing.

2 — Use words from the word bank to help you and write the name of bones being used under each photo. Most of the names of bones will need to be used more than once, under different pictures. Initials have been given to help you.

> Think of the action. For example, is it throwing, which involves the arms, or is it making a landing, and if so, using which part of the body? When you have worked out which part of the body is performing the main task, think of the bones in that region of the body.

a)

- S _____
- U _____
- C _____
- P _____
- H _____
- R _____
- M _____

b)

- S _____
- U _____
- C _____
- P _____
- H _____
- R _____
- M _____

c)

- P _____
- P _____
- F _____
- M _____
- F _____
- T _____
- T _____
- P _____

d)

- H _____
- R _____
- U _____

Word bank

- Pelvis
- Scapula
- Humerus
- Ulna
- Radius
- Carpals
- Metacarpals
- Phalanges
- Femur
- Tibia
- Fibia
- Patella
- Tarsals
- Metatarsals

1.2.5 A healthy, active lifestyle and your skeletal system

Homework 1: Naming bones

Student's Book page 200

Tasks

1 — Label the bones in the skeleton diagram. All the bones that need labelling have a line coming from them and the first letter is given. Use the word bank to remind you of the different names.

2 — Learn the names of the bones of the body. Start by trying to memorize the bones of the upper body. When you feel confident, go on to the bones of the lower body.

> It is sometimes difficult to remember the position of the ulna and radius in the lower arm and the tibia and fibula in the lower leg. If you remember Ulna is Underneath the radius and the Tibia is on Top of the fibula that may help.
> Note the phalanges are both your fingers and your toes!

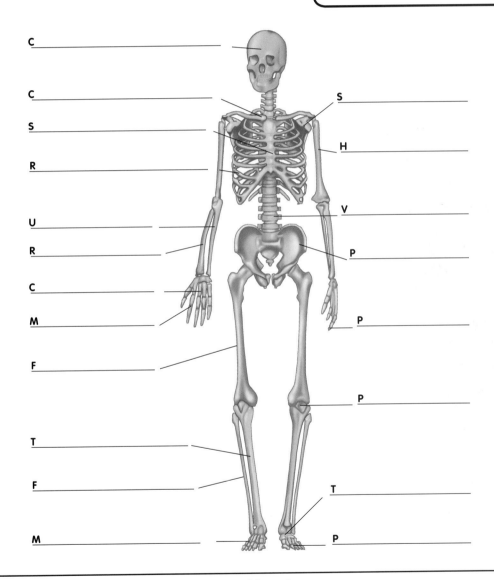

C _____

C _____

S _____

R _____

U _____

R _____

C _____

M _____

F _____

T _____

F _____

M _____

S _____

H _____

V _____

P _____

P _____

P _____

T _____

P _____

Word bank

- Cranium
- Sternum
- Ribs
- Humerus
- Ulna
- Radius
- Femur
- Patella
- Carpals
- Tibia
- Fibula
- Scapula
- Clavicle
- Tarsals
- Metatarsals
- Phalanges
- Vertebrae
- Metacarpals
- Pelvis

1.2.5 A healthy, active lifestyle and your skeletal system

Homework 2: Interpreting information

Student's Book page 197

Task

Study the table about vertebrae below and answer the questions.

	Cervical	Thoracic	Lumbar	Sacral	Coccyx
Number of	7	12	5	5	4
Where in the body	Neck	Chest	Lower back	Pelvic area	Base of the spine
Most important function	Top two vertebrae, atlas and axis, help turn the neck and protect spinal chord.	Attached to the ribs and help with breathing: protect spinal chord.	In the area of the column where the greatest amount of movement occurs so bears a lot of weight. Protect spinal chord, the largest vertebrae in the body.	They are fused together and make up part of the pelvic girdle.	They are fused together to form the base of the spine.
What is attached	Neck muscles	Ribs	Back muscles	Joins spine and pelvic girdle	Base of spine attached only to the sacral vertebrae

a) How many vertebrae are there in total?

_____

b) Which vertebrae are found in the chest region of the body?

_____

c) Which vertebrae are the largest in the body?

_____

d) What is the main job of the thoracic vertebrae?

_____

e) There are two types of vertebrae that are fused. Which are they?

_____

1.2.5 A healthy, active lifestyle and your skeletal system

© Folens (copiable page)

Homework 3: Multiple-choice questions

Student's Book pages 196–201

Tasks

1 — Read the questions below and choose the correct answer. Read the question again to make sure, and then write the letter of the correct answer in the space provided.

1. Which of the following are names of vertebrae?

   a) Sacral, thoracic, lumbar, irregular, coccyx

   b) Lumbar, cervical, clavicle, sacral, thoracic

   c) Cervical, thoracic, lumbar, sacral, coccyx

   d) Cervical, thoracic, lumbar, sternum, coccyx

2. The bones of the lower leg consist of:

   a) Tibia, phalanges, carpals, fibula

   b) Tarsals, phalanges, fibula, tibia

   c) Femur, phalanges, pelvis, tarsals

   d) Fibula, tarsals, clavicle, tibia

3. Functions of the skeleton involve:

   a) Protecting organs of the body and giving the body its general shape

   b) Production of red blood cells and killing bacteria

   c) Helping with movement and helping respiration

   d) Supporting tissues of the body and assisting with clotting

4. The following are all flat bones:

   a) Patella, sternum, femur, cranium

   b) Vertebrae, tarsals, clavicle, scapula

   c) Scapula, sternum, pelvis, ribs

   d) Pelvis, sacrum, ribs, tibia

2 — Write out three multiple-choice questions of your own on the other side of this sheet. Use the same method of asking questions as above. Refer to your workbook notes to help you.

Extension 1: Bones that protect

Student's Book pages 210–211

Tasks

1 — List the protecting bones of the skeleton and state what they protect.

_____

_____

_____

_____

_____

_____

_____

_____

2 — Give a sporting example of how each protecting bone can be effective.

_____

_____

_____

_____

_____

_____

_____

_____

3 — State what equipment can be used to further protect the sportsperson. For example: cricket – helmet with grille – protection from bouncers from fast bowlers.

_____

_____

_____

_____

_____

_____

_____

_____

Extension 2: Bones and sport

Student's Book pages 199–201

Task

Work out which words should go in the gaps in the table below. Use your workbook notes as a reference. Include as many examples as possible.

Type of bone	Name of bone	Sporting action
Long bone		Rebounds the ball when playing a volleyball dig
Short bone		
	Sternum	

Extension 3: Questions on bones

Student's Book pages 196–201

Task

Read the following questions carefully. When you have worked out your responses, write full sentences in the spaces provided.

a) There are five functions of the skeleton. Name one of them and briefly explain what it does.

_____

_____

_____

_____

b) Irregular is the name of a type of bone. Give an example of a sporting situation and the relevance of an irregular bone.

_____

_____

_____

_____

c) The lumbar vertebrae are the largest in the spinal column. Briefly explain why this is so.

_____

_____

_____

_____

d) When a player plays an overhead clear in badminton, which bones are mainly involved?

_____

_____

_____

e) The skeleton helps give us our general shape. How will this influence a person deciding on a choice of sports?

_____

_____

_____

_____

1.2.5 A healthy, active lifestyle and your skeletal system

© Folens (copiable page)

Worksheet 5: Names and locations of synovial joints

Level A   **Student's Book pages 196–211**

Task

Fill in the table below by adding:

- the type of joint
- the bones involved

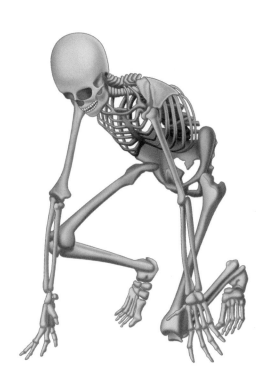

Location	Neck	Knee	Hip	Elbow	Shoulder
Type of joint					
Bones involved					

Worksheet 5: Names and locations of synovial joints

Level B   **Student's Book pages 196–211**

Task

Fill in the table below by adding:

- the type of joint
- the bones involved.

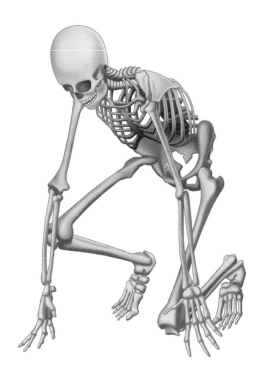

The word bank has all the words you need. The words in bold are used more than once.

Location	Neck	Knee	Hip	Elbow	Shoulder
Type of joint					
Bones involved					

Word bank

- pivot
- humerus
- **ball and socket**
- pelvis
- **femur**
- tibia
- **hinge**
- axis
- scapula
- atlas
- ulna

Worksheet 6: Types of synovial joint

Level A **Student's Book pages 198–206**

Tasks

1 — Look at the illustrations of three athletes below and work out which joint (circled) is involved in the action they are performing. Write the name of the type of joint in the spaces provided.

2 — Add labels to each of the diagrams, giving the names of the bones involved.

a) Long jumper

b) Rugby

c) Badminton

Worksheet 6: Types of synovial joint

Level B   **Student's Book pages 198–206**

Tasks

1 — Look at the illustrations of three athletes below and work out which joint (circled) is involved in the action they are performing. Write the name of the type of joint in the spaces provided.

2 — Add labels to each of the diagrams, giving the names of the bones involved. Use the words from the word bank to help you.

a) Long jumper

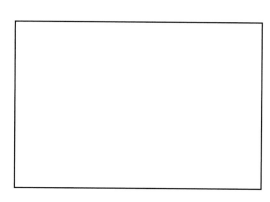

b) Rugby

c) Badminton

Word bank

- atlas
- femur
- scapula
- patella
- tibia
- humerus
- axis

1.2.5 A healthy, active lifestyle and your skeletal system

Worksheet 7: Types of movement at a j[...]

Level A **Student's Book pages 204–209**

Tasks

1 — Number the following joints from the greatest amount of movement to the least, with 1 being the greatest and 5 being the least. Write your answers in the spaces provided.

a) hip ☐

b) shoulder ☐

c) knee ☐

d) elbow ☐

e) neck ☐

2 — Provide a different sporting example that uses the following joints.

a) hip _____

b) shoulder _____

c) knee _____

d) elbow _____

e) neck _____

3 — Give the correct type of joint for each of the following:

a) hip _____

b) shoulder _____

c) knee _____

d) elbow _____

e) neck _____

rksheet 7: Types of movement at a joint

Level B   **Student's Book pages 204–209**

Tasks

1 — Number the following joints from the greatest amount of movement to the least, with 1 being the greatest and 5 being the least. Write your answers in the spaces provided.

a) hip ☐

b) shoulder ☐ 2

c) knee ☐

d) elbow ☐ 5

e) neck ☐

> Two have been completed already to help you.

2 — Provide a different sporting example that uses the following joints.

a) hip _____

b) shoulder _____

c) knee _____

d) elbow _____

e) neck _____

3 — Give the correct type of joint for each. Use the word bank to help you.

a) hip _____

b) shoulder _____

c) knee _____

d) elbow _____

e) neck _____

Word bank

- Ball and socket
- Hinge
- Pivot
- Hinge
- Ball and socket

Worksheet 8: Action/movement/joint

Level A **Student's Book pages 198–209**

Tasks

1 — Look at the table below about types of movement and the joints involved with various sporting actions.

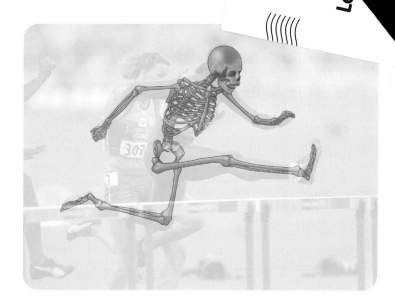

2 — Fill in the table, using the example as a guide.

Example	Area	Type of joint	Type of movement	Description of the action
Kicking a football	Knee	Hinge	Extension	Lower leg moves forward to straighten after contact with the ball.
Hurdler lifting lead leg to clear a hurdle				
Swimmer performing front crawl arm action				
Shooting arm action when scoring in basketball or netball				

ksheet 8: Action/movement/joint

el B **Student's Book pages 198–209**

Tasks

1 — Look at the table below about types of movement and the joints involved with various sporting actions. The three sporting actions are:

- hurdler lifting lead leg to clear a hurdle
- swimmer performing front crawl arm action
- arm action required when shooting a basket or goal in netball.

> Use the word bank to help you. All words are used once.

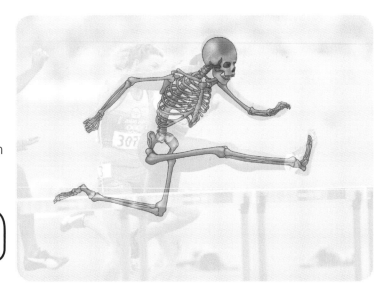

2 — Fill in the table, using the example as a guide.
In the final column you should use your own words to give a brief description of the action.

Example	Area	Type of joint	Type of movement	Description of the action
Kicking a football	Knee	Hinge	Extension	Lower leg moves forward to straighten after contact with the ball.
Hurdler lifting lead leg to clear a hurdle				
Swimmer performing front crawl arm action				
Shooting arm action when scoring in basketball or netball				

Word bank

- Pelvis
- Shoulder
- Ball and socket
- Elbow
- Rotation
- Hinge
- Rotation
- Extension
- Ball and socket

1.2.5 A healthy, active lifestyle and your skeletal system   © Folens (copiable page)

Worksheet 9: Linking muscles to sport

Level A   **Student's Book pages 196–209**

Task

Complete the table below. Follow the example to help you.

Muscle name	Type of movement	Sport example	Description of action
Biceps	Flexion	Basketball	Flexion of elbow as player prepares to shoot
Triceps			
Deltoids			
Pectorals			
Trapezius			
Latissimus dorsi			
Abdominals			
Gluteals			
Quadriceps			
Hamstring			
Gastrocnemius			

Worksheet 9: Linking muscles to sport

Level B   **Student's Book pages 196–209**

Task

Complete the table below. Some of the answers have been given to help you.

Muscle name	Type of movement	Sport example	Description of action
Biceps	Flexion	Basketball	Flexion of elbow as player prepares to shoot
Triceps			
Deltoids		Golf	
Pectorals			During the pull phase of breast-stroke arm action
Trapezius	Abduction		
Latissimus dorsi			Bring arms in during pull phases when rowing
Abdominals			
Gluteals			As angle at hip increases, the weightlifter comes to a standing position
Quadriceps			
Hamstring		Sprinting	
Gastrocnemius	Extension		

1.2.5 A healthy, active lifestyle and your skeletal system   © Folens (copiable page)

Homework 4: Description of movement at a joint

Student's Book pages 204–206

Tasks

1 — Read the following three descriptions of movements at a joint. In each case, identify the joint being described and link the description with a sporting action.

a) • Circle 360°
    • Two different types in the body
    • Have the greatest range of movement in the body

_____

b) • Can move in two directions
    • Ligaments help to stabilize this joint
    • Most robust joint

_____

c) • Helps rotate and tilt
    • Involves two specialized bones
    • Occurs at the top of the vertebral column

_____

2 — Now make up two more sets of phrases for two different joints and link them with a sporting action. Use different ideas from those used above. Name the joint in each case.

_____

_____

_____

_____

_____

_____

_____

_____

Homework 5: Multiple-choice questions on joints

Student's Book pages 202–209

Tasks

1 — Read the following questions and choose the correct answer from those given. Read the question again to make sure and then write the correct letter in the space provided.

1. Bones involved in hinge joints are:

   a) Tibia, femur, scapula, humerus

   b) Ulna, femur, radius, tibia

   c) Radius, scapula, fibula, ulna

   d) Pelvis, phalanges, femur, humerus

2. Parts of a synovial joint are:

   a) Muscle, adduction, cartilage, ligament

   b) Joint capsule, irregular bones, synovial fluid, cartilage

   c) Synovial fluid, hyaline cartilage, ligament, joint capsule

   d) Tendons, ligaments, pelvis, synovial fluid

3. The following are words linked with tendons:

   a) Attach muscle to bone, non-elastic, anchor, strong

   b) Elastic, holds bone in place, at ends of bone, strong

   c) Reduces friction, lubricates, non-elastic, tough fibre

   d) Non-elastic, anchor, strong, lubricates

4. The following are words connected with the hip joint:

   a) Adduction, movement in one direction only, femur, patella

   b) Extension, ball and socket, scapula, femur

   c) Rotation, ball and socket, pelvis, femur

   d) Rotation, pelvis, femur, movement in two directions only

2 — Write out two multiple-choice questions of your own about joints on the other side of this sheet. Use the same method of asking questions as above.

Homework 6: Common injuries

Student's Book pages 214–218

Task

Read the paragraph below about common injuries and fill in the gaps. Use the statements from the statement bank to help you.

Strains and sprains are examples of _____. Strains are to do with _____

and sprains are to do with _____ and _____. Each occurs when rigorous over

_____ and twisting happens. _____ too far to reach a ball in tennis or

_____ at speed in basketball can cause these problems.

Both injuries are treated with RICE. The initials stand for _____, ice, _____

and elevation. These are the _____ and the _____. The

reason to rest the injured part is so that no further _____ is done. Putting ice on the injury

_____. _____ the part also stops the swelling and elevating the injured

part helps with the swelling and stops the _____ too.

Tennis and golf elbow affect the _____ attaching the muscle to the bone at the elbow. This can be caused by

playing the _____ and by using _____ equipment such as the handle on

a tennis racket. Again, RICE is the treatment for this injury.

Statement bank

- compression
- soft tissue injuries
- incorrectly sized
- throbbing
- damage

- stretching
- tendons
- reduces the swelling
- joints
- ligaments

- Compressing
- sport too much
- actions
- muscles

- Striding
- order of treatment
- turning
- rest

Homework 7: Major injuries

Student's Book page 214–218

Task

Fill in the table below, which is about three common injuries. Write how, when and where the injury can happen and how it can be avoided.

Injury	How it happens	When it happens	Where it happens	How to avoid it
Torn cartilage				
Dislocation				
Fracture				

1.2.5 A healthy, active lifestyle and your skeletal system

Homework 8: Torn cartilage, dislocation and fractures

Student's Book pages 214–218

Task

Study the sentences below in relation to torn cartilage, dislocation and fractures injuries. Reorder the text for each of the named injuries, putting numbers in the boxes before each sentence to indicate the correct order.

Dislocation

- [ ] a) The player suffers extreme pain.
- [ ] b) The joint at the elbow dislocates as a result.
- [ ] c) The rugby player receives the ball and runs towards the try line.
- [ ] d) The joint looks deformed.
- [ ] e) As they land, the player in possession lands heavily on their arm.
- [ ] f) They are made comfortable, their arm is immobilized and they are taken to hospital.
- [ ] g) An opposition member makes a running tackle on them.

Fractures

- [ ] a) The casualty is made comfortable and kept warm, to prevent hypothermia.
- [ ] b) On landing, the person's tibia strikes a boulder.
- [ ] c) The force breaks the bone but it does not penetrate the skin.
- [ ] d) The fall is six metres from a ridge to a lower rock outcrop.
- [ ] e) Medical help is called for immediately.
- [ ] f) The area becomes tender and swollen.
- [ ] g) Whilst a group of mountaineers do some bouldering, one of the party takes a fall.

Torn cartilage

- [ ] a) The player cannot move their knee joint.
- [ ] b) RICE is applied and if the injury is severe they are taken to hospital.
- [ ] c) The force of their body landing and the joint having to bend in the wrong direction causes the cartilage to tear.
- [ ] d) As they land, they turn their body to make the interception.
- [ ] e) A player running, at pace, to intercept the basketball sees the ball going behind them.
- [ ] f) The player is in lots of pain.

Extension 4: Synovial joints and the sportsperson

Student's Book pages 202–209

Tasks

1 — How does the design of the synovial joint aid the sportsperson?

_____

_____

_____

_____

_____

_____

Hyaline cartilage
reduces friction, acts as a shock absorber

Fibrous joint capsule

Ligament
joins bone to bone

Muscle

Tendon
joins muscle to bone, enabling movement

Synovial membrane
produces synovial fluid

Synovial membrane
produces synovial fluid

2 — Choose six sporting actions and complete the table below by:

- naming the sport the action comes from
- stating which synovial joint is mainly involved
- describing the action.

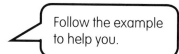
Follow the example to help you.

Sport	Sporting action	Synovial joint involved	Description of the action
Football	Glancing header	Pivot joint at the neck	As contact with the ball is made the head moves out and to the side to direct the ball.

Extension 5: Types of movement and sports actions

Student's Book pages 207–209

Tasks

1 — List the five types of movement afforded by synovial joints:

1) _____

2) _____

3) _____

4) _____

5) _____

2 — Thomas is a keen basketball player and is able to successfully complete many skills required in the game. Choose four skills from basketball and describe the type of movement and the joints involved.

For example: intercepting a pass – abduction – arms move away from the body to perform the action – ball and socket at shoulder and hinge joint at elbow plus hinge joints at fingers.

a) _____

_____

_____

_____

b) _____

_____

_____

_____

c) _____

_____

_____

_____

d) _____

_____

_____

_____

Extension 6: Questions requiring short answers

Student's Book pages 203–209

Tasks

1 — Read the following questions carefully. Pick out the key words, think and then answer each one in the space provided.

a) What is the name for freely moveable joints?

_____

b) Which type of joint is found at the elbow?

_____

c) The shoulder is one example of a ball and socket joint. What is another?

_____

d) If tendons attach bone to muscle, what do ligaments do?

_____

_____

e) What is the opposite movement to adduction?

_____

f) What is the name for the movement that reduces the angle at a joint?

_____

g) Which movement is in action when performing front crawl?

_____

h) When does flexibility become difficult to maintain?

_____

_____

2 — Now make up two questions of your own that require one-word answers.

_____

_____

_____

_____

_____

_____

_____

_____

_____

The skeleton

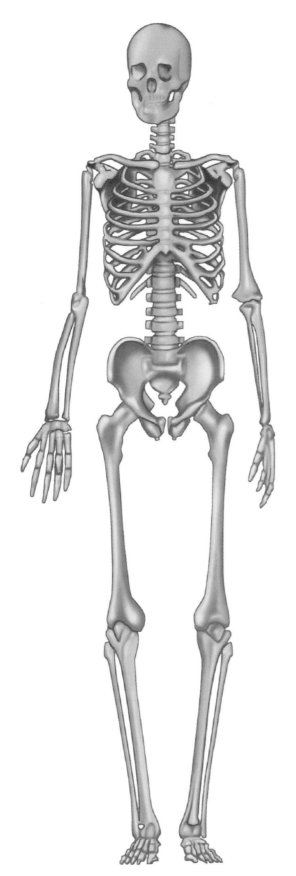

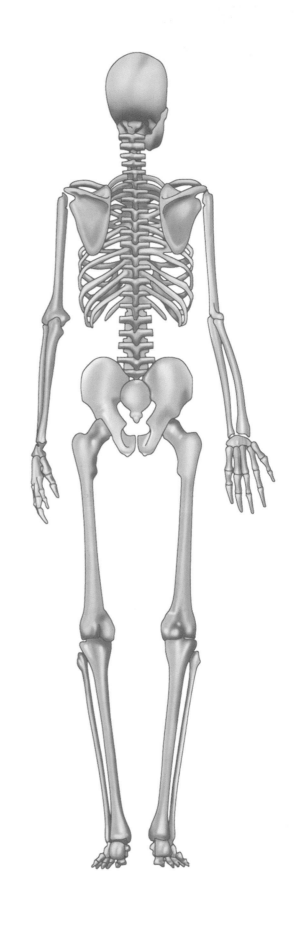

The synovial joint of the knee

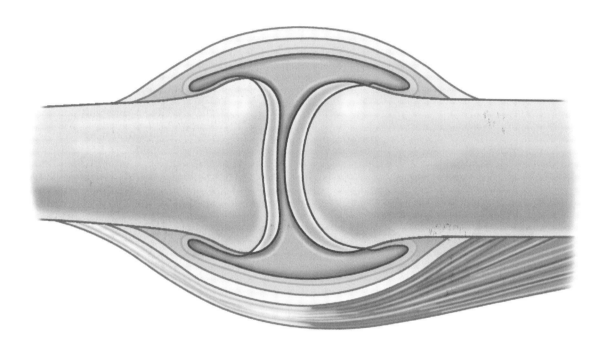

1.2.5 A healthy, active lifestyle and your skeletal system

Joints of the body

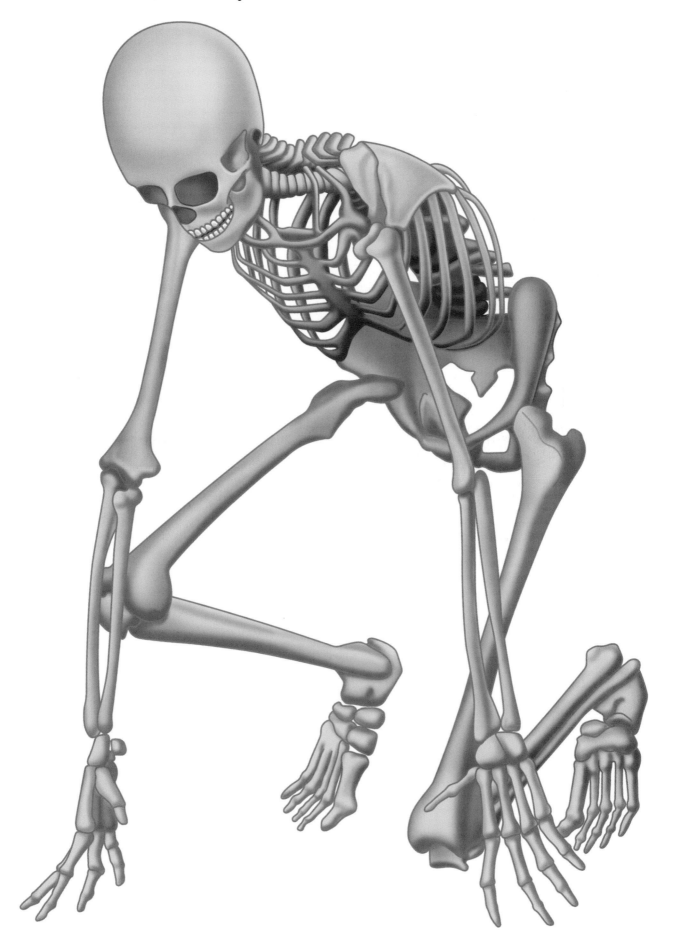

1.2.5 A healthy, active lifestyle and your skeletal system

Answer section
Contents

Answers

© Folens (copiable page)

1.1 — Healthy, active lifestyles

1.1.1 Healthy, active lifestyles and how they could benefit you

Worksheet 1: Positive effects of exercise, Level B

1. d, i   **2.** b, n   **3.** h, m   **4.** g, o

5. f, l   **6.** a, p   **7.** e, k   **8.** c, j

Homework 1: Why do people take part in sport?

1. Rugby player – b, c, h   **2.** Middle-distance runner – a, d, f   **3.** Leisure club member – e, g, i

Extension 1: Positive effects of physical activity

Helps physical development
- Helps a person to look and feel good
- Provides a physical challenge
- Can help relieve stress and tension
- Helps to improve body shape
- Contributes to good health
- Allows a person to take part in a sport

Helps mental development
- Provides enjoyment
- Can provide stimulation and excitement
- Gives opportunities for aesthetic appreciation
- Provides opportunity for competition

Helps social development
- Encourages social mixing
- Gain membership to a particular sports club
- Improves team and cooperation skills
- Encourages friendship

1.1.2 Influences on your healthy, active lifestyle

Worksheet 1: Parents, teachers and peers, Levels A and B

Parent
- You'll be the only one that does not play!
- I played for the local team just like my father.
- We will give you the chance to experience the use of local facilities.

Teacher
- I can show you how to live a healthy life.
- You will have the opportunity to take part in sport at different levels.
- I can see ability in you, so try this sport.

Peer
- What are you scared of?
- We lacked confidence at the beginning, but once we got to know people it was fine.
- Come with us – you'll really enjoy it!

Worksheet 2: Social reasons affecting participation, Levels A and B

2. **a)** C   **b)** A   **c)** C   **d)** B   **e)** C

     f) A   **g)** B   **h)** C   **i)** B

3. (Level A only)
Possible answers include:
- travelling to facilities
- access to facilities
- integrating in general sessions

Worksheet 3: Joining a club, Level B

2. a) The facilities at our club are the best in the county.
  b) Membership is rising fast, since the new coach arrived.
  c) The people at the club are so friendly; we always go out for a drink after the matches.
  d) I feel so relaxed, satisfied and calm after a good workout.
  e) By joining the club, it means that we can come and play whenever we like.
  f) I never thought I was competitive until I started to join in the club competitions.
  g) I was shy to begin with, but the people at the club made me feel so welcome that I have grown in confidence.

Worksheet 5: Experience different ways to enjoy sport, Level B

2. a) healthy life
  c) providing extra time
  e) I am responsible for recording
  g) communication skills
  b) broad range of experiences
  d) experience of being the leader
  f) compose my own routines
  h) tests my knowledge of the rules

Homework 1: Female role models

Possible answers include:
- Rebecca Adlington would give a wholesome image to the product being advertised.
- She is seen as a role model to look up to and emulate. This in turn can encourage people to lead a healthy lifestyle, which includes exercise.
- The activity associated with her is brought to the public eye too. The effect can make that activity more popular.
- People make the link between a successful woman and a successful company.

Extension 1: The sports participation pyramid

2.
- Foundation – school – about 5–16 – Physical education/Dragon sport/Active recreation – recreational
- Participation – school/leisure centres/fitness clubs – about 11–18 – team/club participation
- Performance – local clubs/regional centres – about 16+ – coaching, training and competition at regional level
- Elite – National centres of excellence and international centres – about 16+ – coaching, training and competition to national and international level.

Extension 3: Different roles in sport: clubs and committees

- Results secretary – Inform of scores and league position
- Governing body/council representative – Represent the players in meetings
- Captain/vice captain – Play in full range of games in a season
- Secretary – Record meetings
- Chairperson – Run and keep order in a meeting
- Treasurer – Keep check on club finances
- Community officer – Create links with various groups

1.1.3 Exercise and fitness as part of your healthy, active lifestyle

Worksheet 1: Sporting activities and health-related exercise, Level A

1. Possible answers include:

Component	Positive effects	Negative effects
Cardiovascular fitness	The body can meet the demands of exercise and keep working without losing skill such as in skiing.	Body cannot transport oxygen to the working muscles so they tire easily before the end of the race.
Muscular strength	The vaulter has a good grip and can pull his body weight to help clear the bar.	Poor hand strength prevents the vaulter keeping a grip on the pole.
Muscular endurance	Allows the rower to keep form throughout the race without tiring.	The rower will not be able to keep to the standard required.
Flexibility	The jumper can arch their back to clear the bar.	Poor flexibility limits the amount the back can arch and could lead to the competitor knocking the bar off.
Body composition	A tall netball player will be able to reach to defend the shots.	A shorter, heavier player may not be able to keep up with the goal shooter and prevent them scoring.

Worksheet 2: Components of skill-related fitness, Levels A and B

1. a) Power   **b)** Agility   **c)** Balance   **d)** Reaction time   **e)** Speed   **f)** Coordination

2. Gymnastics – balance, agility and power;
Hockey – speed, power and agility;
Javelin – power, speed and coordination;
Golf – coordination, balance and power;
Racket sports – agility, power and reaction time;
Running – speed, power and reaction time.

Worksheet 3: skilled performance, Levels A and B

1.
- Efficiency: minimal effort/thought/time
- Pre-determined: skills practised/performed in predicted situations/maximum certainty of success
- Coordinated: control of large and small muscles/perform complex skills
- Fluent: graceful/ease/fluent movements
- Aesthetic: whole action looks good

Homework 1: Effects of health-related exercise on skill-related fitness

Possible answers include:
- **Cardiovascular fitness:** link the length of the event/match/extra time keeping oxygen to working muscles so they can still function – coordination/reaction time.
- **Muscular strength:** using body weight as resistance/power/balance – strength of muscles keeping body balanced.
- **Muscular endurance:** muscles cannot function if not trained – lack of oxygen present/lactic acid build up/link with length of event – if trained keep working over long periods – coordination/reaction time/power/speed.
- **Flexibility:** joints able to move in full range – player can stretch for the ball/gymnastics able to assume difficult positions/able to keep agile and balanced.
- **Body composition:** can affect the range of movement available so affect agility.

Extension 1: Health-related exercise and sports

2.

	Sprinter	Gymnast	Marathon runner	Hockey player
Cardiovascular fitness	10	10	8	8
Muscular endurance	0	0	10	7
Muscular strength	7	10	0	6
Flexibility	9	8	6	6
Body composition	7	9	9	7

3. Possible answers include:
- Sprinter – combines strength with speed for power.
- Gymnast – flexibility required for different positions.
- Marathon runner – keep standard over long events using cardiovascular fitness.
- Hockey player – all necessary without extremes.

Extension 2: Health-related exercise components

2. a) move the joints to the full range of movement.

b) tiring, losing effectiveness or reaching their maximum effort load.

c) apply force and overcome resistance.

d) supply oxygen to the working muscles over long periods of time.

e) is the fastest rate a person can complete a task or cover a distance.

3. Possible answers include:
- A gymnast needs flexibility to move their joints through the full range in order to achieve the correct body shape required for their sport.
- Tennis players need muscular endurance to play well throughout a long match in order to win.
- A javelin thrower needs muscular strength combined with speed to make a throw powerful and get good distance.
- Rugby players need cardiovascular fitness to keep their muscles supplied with oxygen so they can work effectively and perform skills effectively in the game.
- A football goalkeeper needs the correct body composition – height and weight – in order to be effective in goal.

1.1.4a Physical activity as part of your healthy, active lifestyle: training principles and goal setting

Worksheet 1: Principles and planning, Levels A and B

1. Training principles are important because they:
- Plan for the individual
- Are safe for individuals as exercises are set for them so helps to avoid injury
- Can specify which part of the body is to be improved
- Encourage an understanding of the body systems in order to get the programme right
- Can gradually increase the intensity of the programme
- Can be progressive so the stages are not too large and lead to injury
- Are specific to the activity
- Help plan for progress

Worksheet 2: Classifying principles, Level A

2.

S	Muscular strength is improved by matching the actions of the game/event.
PO	The exercise is performed above the threshold of training.
PO	Further training has to be planned.
S	Exercise matches the actions of the sport.
RR	Effects of training are lost three times faster than any gain made.
PO	After six weeks, training changes to become harder.
PO	Exercise becomes more intense by increasing the frequency, intensity and time.
PO	Changes made to the programme are gradual to avoid injury.
RR	Muscle tissue and cells have time to repair.
RR	Injury or illness can stop training and so the athlete loses fitness.
S	Training is at the pace of a competitive game.
RR	If training stops, muscles atrophy.
I	Training programmes are designed around a person's fitness and needs.
PO	Body works harder than normal.

Worksheet 2: Classifying principles, Level B

a) Specificity
b) Progressive overload
c) Progressive overload
d) Specificity
e) Rest and recovery
f) Progressive overload
g) Progressive overload
h) Progressive overload
i) Rest and recovery
j) Rest and recovery
k) Specificity
l) Rest and recovery
m) Individual differences/needs
n) Progressive overload

Worksheet 3: The FITT principle, Levels A and B

1. a) Frequency
b) Intensity
c) Time
d) Type
e) Specificity
f) F – Frequency
g) Gradual increases in exercise undertaken
h) 60–80 per cent

2. a) five
b) 20
c) 60–80 per cent
d) 80 per cent
e) progressive overload
f) atrophy
g) moderation

Homework 1: Principle of progressive overload

- more than usual
- gradual
- threshold of training
- FITT
- frequency
- how difficult
- length of the session
- type

Extension 1: Three principles

Specificity
- matching
- same way
- same speed
- actions at that pace
- no better substitute

Progressive overload
- more than usual
- threshold of training
- FITT
- frequency
- how difficult
- length of the session
- type
- improve and adjust
- demanding
- testing
- systematically planned

Reversibility

- training stops
- atrophy
- shape and tone
- less time

Extension 2: Two principles

Specifity
- If the skills are practised too slowly then only actions at that pace will be reproduced.
- For specific, skilled activities, such as cycling, there is no substitute activity for the competitor.
- This principle relies on the activity matching the actions used in the game.
- The actions must be performed in the same way and at the same speed as the competition.

Progressive overload
- By regularly performing the training session, the body will improve and adjust.
- The session can be systematically planned to add the necessary changes.
- Changes will include adjustments to FITT.
- By testing the athlete at the beginning of the programme and five to six weeks later, changes the body has made can be recorded.
- After weeks of successful training the sessions need to be made more demanding.

Extension 3: Short test

1. Frequency, Intensity, Time and Type

2. • Frequency – how often the exercise is done in a week
   • Intensity – how difficult the exercise is
   • Time – how long the exercise session lasts
   • Type – the particular exercises used

3. The gradual exercising of the body more than it is normally used to.

4. Training threshold

5. a) Atrophy   **b)** Reversibility

6. 80 per cent

1.1.4b Physical activity as part of your healthy, active lifestyle: assessing fitness and developing an exercise programme

Worksheet 1: Interval training, Levels A and B

1.

After a complete warm-up:	
Time	**Activity**
0–15 secs	bursts of sprints
15–60 secs	**slow running**
60–75 secs	bursts of sprints
75–120 secs	slow running
120–135 secs	**bursts of sprints**
135–180 secs	slow running
180–195 secs	**bursts of sprints**
195–240 secs	**slow running**
240–255 secs	bursts of sprints
255–435 secs	slow running between sets
Each set takes **7 minutes 15 secs** to complete. The whole session repeats four sets of the above.	

2. a) Swimming; any game's skill   **b)** 29 minutes   **c)** Stopwatch

Worksheet 2: Circuit training, Levels A and B

Possible answers include:

- Football: heading; kicking to a target; dribbling round cones; kicking and trapping the ball; kick ups; throw on against a wall to a target; dribble and pass against a bench, collect and dribble back; chipping to a target; two touch against a bench; run, pass ball against a bench, control and stop ball, run back and repeat.
- Basketball: dribbling the ball to a line and back; ball circles around the waist; set shots to a ring; rebound jumps against a wall/backboard; dribble and turn round a cone; bounce passes against a wall; static dribbling using both hands; chest passes against a wall; lay up shots; dribble and pass against a wall.
- Hockey: pass against a bench; Indian dribble round cones; pass and control against a bench/wall; dribble and shoot; flick to a target; pass ball between markers; static tap and reverse stick ball control; dribble, pass and run to collect; pushing ball to a target; reverse stick against the wall/bench.

Worksheet 3: Weight training, Levels A and B

1. regularly; used to the weights; adapted; gradually; progressively; repetitions; sets; three; repetitions; completed; weight

2. a) free (FW)	**b)** both (B)	**c)** free (FW)	**d)** machine (M)
e) both (B)	**f)** machine (M)	**g)** free (FW)	**h)** machine (M)
i) both (B)	**j)** machine (M)	**k)** free (FW)	**l)** machine (M)
m) free (FW)	**n)** both (B)	**o)** free (FW)	**p)** machine (M)

Worksheet 4: Fartlek training, Levels A and B

1.

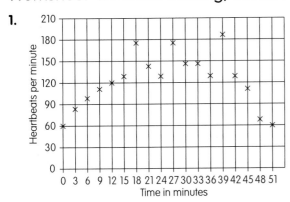

2. speed play; Swedish; woodland; hillsides; sand dunes; vary; intensity; anaerobic respiration; recover; aerobic system; match; games; cycling; swimming; adapts; frequently; harder level; rests; progressing; FITT.

Worksheet 5: Fartlek, cross and continuous training, Levels A and B

- (Hockey player) Fartlek – "I enjoy training outside." "My event needs me to change speeds." "I have good aerobic and anaerobic fitness."
- (Long-distance runner) Continuous – "I like to work on the rower and the stepper." "I need to improve my cardiovascular systems training methods." "I am exercising for my general health."
- (Jogger) Cross – "I like to vary the way I train." "My general fitness is important to me." "My joints are not what they used to be so I change activities to rest them."

Worksheet 6: Personal Exercise Programme (PEP), Levels A and B

1.
1. What is the purpose of the training?
2. Take into account the age of the person.
3. Take into account the experience of the person.
4. Has the person got any training preferences?
5. Understand the pulse and find the resting pulse.
6. Find out how efficient the lungs are by working out the VO_2 max.
7. Assess the ability of the person in several areas by testing various skills.
8. Analyse test.
9. Set tasks for the subject.
10. Re-assess by checking the effects of the exercise on the original test results.

Worksheet 7: Warm-up, Levels A and B

1. Possible answers include:
   a) gradually gets body ready for action, increasing intensity to match the sport; raises body temperature; raises the pulse near to the working pulse rate; concentrates the mind; chance to practise basic skills of the sport/activity; reduces the risk of injury in the activity; start to work as a team; creates a link between rest and the main activity
   b) Cardiovascular warm-up; stretching; flexibility exercises

2. a) Cool-down   **b)** Main activity   **c)** Warm-up
   d) Main activity   **e)** Cool-down   **f)** Warm-up

Worksheet 8: Testing protocol, Levels A and B

- **Reliability:** consistent; procedures; recorded; compared; motivated; tired; meal; conditions; season
- **Validity:** meaningfully; measure; relevant; reflection
- **Comparison:** way; legitimately; past; recognized
- **Safety:** conducting; correct; surface; clothing; equipment; lighting

Worksheet 9: Testing and measuring, Levels A and B

1.

Component of health-related exercise	Type of test	Area tested	Anatomical name for area tested
Muscular strength	Hand grip test	Grip or forearm strength	The extensors and flexor of the lower arm
Cardiovascular fitness	Cooper's 12-minute run test	Heart and lungs	Cardiorespiratory systems
Muscular endurance	Harvard Step test	Leg muscles	Quadriceps
Flexibility	Sit and reach flexibility test	Muscles of lower back	Latissimus dorsi and hamstrings

Homework 1: Circuit training

a) A   **b)** D   **c)** A   **d)** A   **e)** D   **f)** A   **g)** A   **h)** A   **i)** A   **j)** A

Homework 2: Fartlek training

2. a) 185   **b)** 12 minutes   **c)** three times
   d) 18, 27, 39 minutes   **e)** 51 minutes   **f)** two
   g) the heart rate falls   **h)** 21–24 minutes and 30–36 minutes   **i)** to give the body a chance to recover
   j) 42 minutes   **k)** nine minutes

Extension 1: Interval training

3. Possible answers include:
- Dribble – shoot, jog back
- Dribbling round cones – jog back
- Playing a shot – running back to a queue
- Any appropriate and logical 'perform, jog and wait' practices.

Extension 2: Circuit training

Answers to include: cycling, varying time/distance/intensity lasting for over 20 minutes.

1.1.5 Your personal health and well-being

Worksheet 1: Nutrients, Levels A and B

1. a) Instant energy provider   **b)** Body builder and tissue repair
c) Store energy   **d)** Maintaining general health

2. Possible answers include:
a) Fruit, liver, carrots, vegetable oils   **b)** Cakes, beer, bread, pasta   **c)** Meat, fish, beans, nuts

3. a) Carbohydrate loading for endurance events   **b)** Repair tissue after injury
c) Keep the balance of fluids in the body   **d)** As an insulator in extreme weather conditions

4. Sugars and starches – stored as glycogen

Worksheet 2: Marathon runners and diet, Level A

Possible answers include:
a) Carbohydrate loading – allows carbs to be stored as glycogen   **c)** fluids/energy drinks taken in
b) Two hours before event, eat a small carbohydrate meal   **d)** high-energy food taken in

Worksheet 2: Marathon runners and diet, Level B

a) 9   **b)** 5   **c)** 2   **d)** 6   **e)** 10
f) 1   **g)** 7   **h)** 3   **i)** 8   **j)** 4

Worksheet 3: Sports and diet, Levels A and B

1. a) C   **b)** E   **c)** D
d) B   **e)** A   **f)** F

3. (Level A only)
Possible answers include:

Carbohydrate loading
- Linked with long-distance events
- Carbs are easy to digest
- Provide instant source of energy
- Eating more carbs = store of glycogen = reduce levels of fatigue in competition
- Helps maintain performance over a long period of time

High protein
- Used for quick weight loss
- Good for rehabilitation after injury
- Suits rugby players wanting to reduce fat and build up muscle
- Reduces stores of fat in the body

Homework 1: Energy requirements

Table B

Activities (high energy first)	Kilojoules (kJ)	Kilocalories (kcal)
Running	2033	484
Circuit training	1806	430
Cycling	1806	430
Tennis	1579	376
Ice skating	1579	376
Swimming	1357	323
Gardening	1016	242
Mowing the lawn	1016	242
Water aerobics	903	215
Walking	903	215
Housework	790	188
Weight lifting	676	161

Source: Health Discovery, based on a person weighing 112 lbs, exercising for 60 minutes.

Extension 1: Diet and the sportsperson

E = everyday; LD = long-distance athlete; R = rugby player

Toast E LD
Lamb chop E R
Brown rice E LD
Grilled fish E R
Pasta E LD
Lettuce E LD R

Bacon E R
Fried eggs E R
Baked beans E LD R
Fruit E LD R
Boiled potato E LD
Mashed potato E LD

Peas E R
Sausages E R
Carrots E R
Cauliflower E LD R
Tomatoes E LD R

Cucumber E LD R
Jacket potato E LD R
Cake E LD
Gammon ham E R
Lean minced beef E LD R

Extension 2: Diet test

1. Carbohydrates, proteins, fats, vitamins, minerals, fibre and water

2. a) 1000 kcal   **b)** 2119 kcal   **c)** 2381 kcal   **d)** 2667 kcal

3. • Week before event: as training reduces, increase carbohydrate intake;
   • Day before the event: load up on carbohydrates;
   • On the day of the event: eat larger carbohydrate meal three–four hours before race or lighter meal no less than two hours before event and ensure body fluid levels are high;
   • During the event, take in fluids to stop dehydration, replace fluid loss with energy drinks and eat high energy food;
   • Later, a sensible meal should be eaten, depending on the training programme.

4. Raises cholesterol levels; kidney damage for those using high-protein diets for weight loss; possible heart disease, stroke, diabetes and cancer.

5. Reduces flexibility; limits amount of movement which interfere with technique; lowers endurance capability due to having to carry extra weight; reduces speed; affects long-term health including heart disease, high blood pressure and cancer.

1.2.1 Physical activity and your healthy mind and body

Worksheet 1: Somatotypes: body characteristics awareness, Levels A and B

1. a) ectomorph   **b)** mesomorph   **c)** mesomorph/endomorph
   d) mesomorph   **e)** ectomorph   **f)** ectomorph   **g)** mesomorph

2. a) Centre in netball   **b)** Swimmer   **c)** Sprinter
   d) Jockey   **e)** Gymnast   **f)** Prop in rugby
   g) Marathon runner

Worksheet 2: Effects of drugs, Levels A and B

1. a) physically demanding; calm the nerves   **d)** as a relaxant; a steady hand and a calm nerve
   b) socially acceptable; impair judgement   **e)** muscle size; bone growth; recover from injury quicker
   c) masking agent

2. (Level A only) Possible answers include:

Personal pressure; fan pressure; peer pressure; natural ability not enough; need for acclaim; desire for high earnings based on results; win at all costs; make most of a short sporting life; desire to be best at all costs; recover quicker from injury

Worksheet 3: Safety in sport, Levels A and B

1. Possible answers include:
- Javelin and shot put: all competitors drilled in safety measures – carrying equipment, area to wait in, procedure to retrieve/designated area for javelins/shot not in use, marked out and marshalled areas
- Long jump: competitors drilled for safety – waiting area/run up, take-off and landing area checked to be clear and free from obstacles and objects/take-off board in good condition

2. Possible answers include:

Safety equipment in clear view and correctly marked and stored/depth change clearly marked on wall and pool side/pool surround clean and free from obstacles/swim aids neat and safely stored.

Worksheet 4: Outdoor and adventurous activities, Levels A and B

Possible answers include:

Activity	Specialized safety equipment	How the equipment makes the activity safe
Mountaineering	Cagoule/waterproof jacket	Helps to keep the wearer dry and so reduce heat loss.
	Boots	Give a good grip and protect feet, especially ankle, from rough terrain.
Rock climbing	Rope/carabiners	Secures climber to belay so if they lose hold they will not fall far.
	Helmet	Protects head from falling rock.
Canoeing	Helmet	Helps to protect the head if the wearer capsizes.
	Buoyancy aid	If wearer capsizes, they are kept afloat.
Sailing/windsurfing	Wetsuit	Keeps the body temperature warm for long periods.
	All-weather protective suit	Protects from severe weather conditions.
Orienteering	Whistle	To use to attract attention if in difficulty.
	Compass/map	With the correct training, together they pinpoint the orienteer's position.

Worksheet 5: Safety rules, Levels A and B

Possible answers include:
1. Check the conditions for play are safe; check the players are dressed safely; see that the rules of the game are kept; ensure safe play; if conditions change, make decision accordingly; discipline the players
2. Third party – hockey; Blocking – basketball; Contact on the goalie – football; Length of fingernails – Netball; Bouncers too low order batsmen – cricket; Safety throwing areas – athletics; Staying in lane – athletics.

Homework 1: Hazards and playing areas

Possible answers include:
- Litter causing cuts, falls, abrasions
- Personal presentation including untied laces, sharp fingernails, jewellery, no shin pads
- Unbalanced competition: a big boy versus a small boy
- Mix of sports causing balls to fly into other games
- Conditions of area: fence, posts, surface unsuitable for netball, divots to trip on
- Spectators are too close, causing trips, falls or are intimidating
- A dog causing trips and falls

Homework 2: Safety clothing and equipment

Cricketer: helmet; gloves; pads; abdominal protector (box); thigh pad and inner thigh pad; arm guard; chest guard.
Hockey goalkeeper: helmet; hand protectors; kickers; leg guards; body armour/chest protector; padded shorts/smock.

Extension 1: Somatotypes

Ectomorph	Mesomorph	Endomorph
Jockey	Badminton player	Sumo wrestler
Badminton player	Hockey player	
Long-distance runner	Sprinter	
Basketball player	Basketball player	
	Gymnast	
	Footballer	

Extension 2: Banned substances: the facts

	Drugs in this category	Which athlete would use this drug?	The effect on the athlete	Side effects/dangers
Anabolic steroids	Testosterone Nandrolone Stanozonol Boldenone Clenbuterol	Any needing large muscle mass	Allows harder training sessions, increases aggression, helps rehabilitation from injury	Mood swings Men: impotence Women: infertility
Stimulants	Amphetamines Ephedrine Caffeine Cocaine Nicotine	Any athlete relying on reactions and wanting to train harder	Reduces feeling of tiredness and speeds up reactions	Irritability, sleeplessness, high blood pressure, irregular heart beat
Diuretics	Furosemide Triamterene Chlortalidone	Jockey/boxer needing to make a certain weight	Reduces fluid retention, causing rapid weight loss	Dehydration, dizziness, muscle cramps, nausea, kidney illness
Peptide hormones	Human growth hormone (HGH) Erythropoietin (EPO)	Athlete needing to develop the body, recover from injury, endurance event competitor	Increases red blood cells for endurance events, develops muscle, reduces tiredness	Inhibits circulation, possibly leading to stroke or heart attack
Beta-blockers	Atenolol Nodolol	Target sport competitors such as golfers, snooker players, archers and pistol shooters	Calms and steadies the hands, slows heart rate down	Reduces heart rate so much that it may stop
Narcotic analgesics	Methadone Pethidine Morphine	Injured performer wanting to continue training	Hides the pain of injury allowing for participation in training or competitions	Loss of concentration, balance and coordination. Greater injury possible

Answers

Extension 3: Safety and officiating

Possible answers for netball include:

- Before the game: playing areas free from obstacles and objects/posts are safe/netting safe/has correct umpire's equipment/no jewellery/nails are safe length/hair tied back.
- During the game: rules are kept to court position of players correct.
- After the game: announces final score/concludes the match safely.

Extension 4: Rules for safety, order and fairness

a) Keeping order

b) Making play fair

c) Making play fair

d) Keeping order

e) Making play fair

f) Keeping order/Making play fair

g) Keeping order/Making play fair

h) Keeping order/Making play fair

i) Keeping order

j) Keeping order

k) Keeping order

l) Safety/Making play fair

m) Keeping order

n) Keeping order

o) Keeping order/Making play fair

p) Safety

1.2.2 A healthy, active lifestyle and your cardiovascular system

Worksheet 1: Learning the parts of the circulatory system, Levels A and B

1.

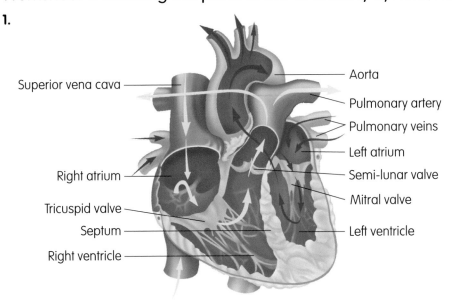

Superior vena cava

Right atrium

Tricuspid valve

Septum

Right ventricle

Aorta

Pulmonary artery

Pulmonary veins

Left atrium

Semi-lunar valve

Mitral valve

Left ventricle

3. (Level A only)
Answers should include:

- Transports oxygen and nutrients.
- Removes waste and toxic products from the body.
- Controls body temperature.
- Protects body by taking antibodies to fight disease at the site of infection.

Worksheet 2: The pathway of blood in the body, Levels A and B

1. Pulmonary artery – out of the heart; Lungs; Pulmonary vein – into the heart; Left atrium; Left ventricle; Aorta – out of the heart; To the body; Vena cava – into the heart; Right atrium; Right ventricle – to the pulmonary artery again

2.

Part of the circulatory system	Pathway
1. Pulmonary artery	Takes deoxygenated blood out of the heart.
2. Lungs	**Blood picks up oxygen and exits lungs via the…**
3. Pulmonary vein	**Takes oxygenated blood to the…**
4. Left atrium	**Oxygenated blood is pumped to the…**

Answers

Part of the circulatory system	Pathway
5. Left ventricle	Takes oxygenated blood out of the heart.
6. Aorta	Takes oxygenated blood away from the heart to the…
7. Body	Oxygen is used by working muscles and then to…
8. Vena cava	Takes deoxygenated blood back to the heart.
9. Right atrium	Pumps deoxygenated blood to the…
10. Right ventricle	Pumps blood out of the heart to the pulmonary artery.

Worksheet 3: Three types of blood vessels, Levels A and B

1.

Artery	Capillary	Vein
Blood enters at a high pressure	—	Works under low pressure
Has a strong pulse	Walls are semi-permeable	Has no pulse
Has thick walls	Walls are one cell thick	Has thin walls
Has an elastic quality	Minute internal diameter	Has a less elastic quality
Takes blood away from the heart	Fed by the arteries at one end	Takes blood to the heart
Mostly carries oxygenated blood	Feeds the veins at the other end	Carries deoxygenated blood
Does not have valves	Does not have valves	Has valves

2. (Level A only)
Possible answers include:
- Artery: thick walls to withstand high blood pressure; flexible for pulse.
- Capillary: thin walls so carbon dioxide can pass through.
- Vein: thinner walls than arteries as they work at low pressure; little pulse so less need for elasticity; have valves to prevent back flow of blood countering the low pressure blood movement.

Worksheet 4: The composition of blood, Levels A and B

1.
- Red blood cells are called erythrocytes.
- The main function of red blood cells is to transport oxygen.
- In the red blood cells is haemoglobin; this helps the transportation of oxygen to the working muscles.
- White blood cells protect the body by going to the source of infection.
- White blood cells are also called leukocytes.
- White blood cells are produced in both the long bones and the lymph tissue of the body.
- The platelets' job is to clot the blood.
- Platelets are smaller parts of larger cells.
- Plasma is 90 per cent water and makes up 55 per cent of the volume of blood.
- Plasma contains plasma proteins that help the circulation between cells and tissue.

2. (Level A only)
Answers should include:

Haemoglobin
- Found in red blood cells
- Chemicals can attach making oxyhaemoglobin
- It is the means by which oxygen is transported to the working muscles

Fibrinogen
- Found in plasma
- Helps clotting
- One of several constituents of plasma

Worksheet 5: Effects of exercise on the heart, Levels A and B

72 beats per minute; resting heart rate; oxygen; stroke volume; cardiac output; increases; 220 – age; 85ml; stroke volume by the heart rate; recovery rate

Worksheet 6: Immediate effects of exercise on the performer, Levels A and B

a) face; dilate   **b)** stroke   **c)** sweats   **d)** blood cells   **e)** muscles

f) Arteries   **g)** heart rate   **h)** Salt   **i)** temperature; heat   **j)** oxygen

Homework 1: Interpreting a graph

a) 140 bpm   **b)** 62 bpm   **c)** 62 bpm

d) aerobic   **e)** after the warm-up   **f)** 12 minutes

g) the pulse rate stays constant   **h)** nine minutes

Homework 2: Questions on the circulatory system

a) After having sat still for a few minutes.

b) Because the body stops its demand for extra blood when sitting down at rest and so slows to the resting pulse.

c) Oxygenated blood.

d) Pulmonary artery.

e) It increases.

f) The working muscles demand more oxygen to work and the waste products need to be removed from the body.

g) Veins.

h) Red blood cells.

Extension 1: Effects of exercise on the heart

Possible answers include:

1. Greater demand of oxygen to working muscles which needs to get there faster.

2. Greater volume of blood pumped so you are more aware.

3. Surface blood vessels dilate (open) to help temperature control.

4. Waste products increase as a result of exercise so are removed by perspiration.

5. Salt is a waste product and removed via perspiration.

6. Reducing exercise reduces demand for oxygen in the muscles so heart rate reduces.

7. Working muscles produce heat – so you'll feel hot.

Extension 2: Interpreting a graph 1

2. a)   **i)** Heart rate increasing during warm-up

     ii) Heart rate increasing and decreasing during period of exercise and rest

     iii) Heart rate decreasing during cool-down

b) Shows the end of warm-up followed by increased intensity exercise

c) Intense period of effort followed by less intense/rest periods

d) Interval training

e) Games players/athletes and so on

Extension 3: Interpreting a graph 2

2. a)   **i)** Heart rate increasing during warm-up

     ii) Heart rate increasing and decreasing during periods of exercise then rest and exercise again

     iii) Period of highest intensity

     iv) Heart rate decreasing during cool-down

b) Shows the end of warm-up followed by increased intensity exercise

c) Varied exercise in time, length and intensity

d) Fartlek training

e) Any games player, such as footballer, hockey player, rugby player and so on

     Answers

1.2.3 A healthy, active lifestyle and your respiratory system

Worksheet 1: Air passages, Levels A and B

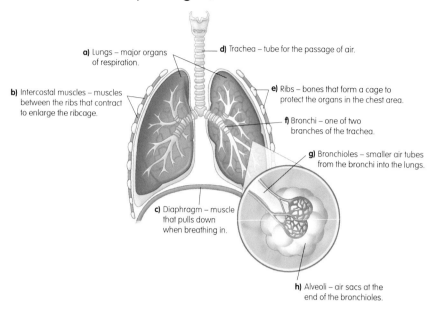

a) Lungs – major organs of respiration.

b) Intercostal muscles – muscles between the ribs that contract to enlarge the ribcage.

c) Diaphragm – muscle that pulls down when breathing in.

d) Trachea – tube for the passage of air.

e) Ribs – bones that form a cage to protect the organs in the chest area.

f) Bronchi – one of two branches of the trachea.

g) Bronchioles – smaller air tubes from the bronchi into the lungs.

h) Alveoli – air sacs at the end of the bronchioles.

Worksheet 2: Mechanisms of breathing, Levels A and B

For Level A mark any logical sentence with the following information:

Inspiration	Expiration
Diaphragm	Diaphragm
Pulls down	Relaxes
Intercostal muscles	Intercostal muscles
Contract	Relax to dome shape
Chest expands	Chest decreases
Pressure decreases	Pressure increases

Worksheet 3: Composition of inhaled and exhaled air, Levels A and B

2.

	Inhaled air	Exhaled air
Oxygen	20%	16%
Carbon dioxide	Trace	4%
Nitrogen	79%	79%

3. a) Because oxygen has been taken in by the body, to be used by the working muscles.
b) Carbon dioxide is toxic (harmful) to the system and is breathed out.

4. (Level A only)
Possible answers include:
Exchange of gases in alveoli more efficient.
Increases vital capacity of the lungs so:
- more air is exhaled so more carbon dioxide leaves the body in one breath
- more oxygen taken in so muscles can work for longer without tiring
- more oxygen taken up for use by the working muscles.

Worksheet 4: Anaerobic respiration, Levels A and B

1. & 2.

Order of events	Letter	Sentence
1	f	She breathes slowly and respires aerobically.
2	a	She breathes quickly and respires aerobically.
3	e	She begins anaerobic respiration in her muscles.
4	d	Lactic acid forms in the muscles.
5	b	The oxygen debt is repaid.
6	c	Her muscles ache.
7	f	She breathes slowly and respires aerobically.

3. (Level A only)

1. 100m hurdles
2. High jump
3. Shot put
4. 200m
5. Long jump
6. Javelin
7. 800m

4. (Level A only)

- Activities using one all-out burst of maximal effort.
- Activities completed in a short space of time – no more than 45–60 seconds.
- Immediately after the activity the athlete may gasp for breath.

Worksheet 5: Changes in the athlete during exercise, Levels A and B

1. a) Ribs – with deeper breathing, ribs move out more
    b) Nose – inhale more frequently
    c) Alveoli – exchange of gases increases
    d) Mouth – exhale more frequently
    e) Diaphragm – pulls down more
    f) Lungs – more air passes in and out of them

3. a) increases slightly
    c) increases due to greater demand for air
    b) hardly changes
    d) is the term for the increase of breathing due to exercise

Homework 1: How breathing works

a) 7   **b)** 2   **c)** 6   **d)** 1
e) 4   **f)** 8   **g)** 3   **h)** 5

Homework 2: Aerobic and anaerobic respiration

a) Their breathing would be deeper and regular.
b) Blood takes oxygen to the working muscles faster, cooling the body.
c) Getting rid of waste water and salt from the body and cooling the body.
d) Lactic acid build-up.
e) Oxygen debt/lactic acid build-up.

Homework 3: Aerobic and anaerobic respiration in various sports

1. a) AN   **b)** AN   **c)** AN   **d)** AN   **e)** AE
    f) AN   **g)** AN   **h)** AE   **i)** AN   **j)** AN

Extension 1: Aerobic and anaerobic training

2.
- Aerobic – any long-distance event
- Anaerobic – athletic field events and sprints
- Mix – team games

Extension 2: Exercise and the respiratory system

a) Increase/breathing noisier/left gasping

b) Increase/body needs more oxygen to working muscles

c) Uses oxygen in muscles already/paid back later/ gasping for breath

d) Will increase as amount of air required has increased

e) Only increases slightly

Extension 3: Long-term effects of training

1. Possible answers include:

Aerobic training

- Exchange of gases more efficient
- Muscles able to work longer at moderate to hard level
- Maintain effort level without tiring
- Vital capacity increased
- More air exhaled – carbon dioxide out
- More oxygen in – to working muscles

Anaerobic training

- Short burst of maximal effort leads to oxygen debt
- Interval training uses anaerobic respiration
- New capillaries are formed
- Heart muscle is strengthened
- Delivery of oxygen is improved, stopping build-up of lactic acid
- All leads to 'oxygen debt tolerance'

2. Long-distance swimming/running/cycling; continuous training/at about 80 per cent of maximum heart rate/ practice starts and finish paces/working alone and with others.

1.2.4 A healthy, active lifestyle and your muscular system

Worksheet 1: Types of muscle, Levels A and B

1.
- Voluntary – striated/consciously controlled/most common
- Involuntary – smooth/automatic/intestines/blood vessels
- Cardiac – heart/involuntary/automatic/never rests

2. (Level A only)
Answers could include:

a)
- Never tires
- Pumps blood to working muscles
- Increased heart rate, depending on activity level to cope with extra demand
- Works automatically

b)
- Determines person's shape
- Can control their movement: the type of actions made
- Size can be developed – increased bulk and strength for sport
- Can be trained to develop skilled performance

Worksheet 2: Linking muscles to a sport, Levels A and B

2. a) Describe bowling action: rotation of the arm, pectorals contract and latissimus dorsi relaxes as the ball is released

b) Describe the sprinting leg action: abdominals contract; as the leg pushes off the ground, gluteals contract. Quadriceps contract to extend the leg whilst the hamstrings contract to flex the leg at the knee

c) Describe the kicking action: hamstrings contract to flex at the knee; gluteals contract as the leg prepares itself; quadriceps contract to extend at the knee on contact; abdominals contract to lift the leg on follow through

Worksheet 3: Diagram of the arm, Levels A and B

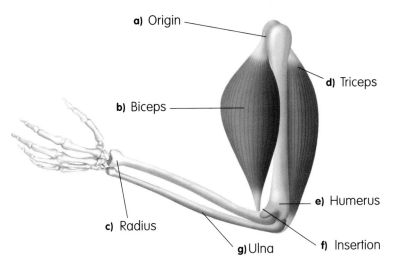

a) Origin
d) Triceps
b) Biceps
e) Humerus
c) Radius
g) Ulna
f) Insertion

Worksheet 4: Diagram of the leg, Levels A and B

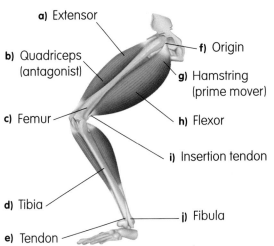

a) Extensor
f) Origin
b) Quadriceps (antagonist)
g) Hamstring (prime mover)
c) Femur
h) Flexor
i) Insertion tendon
d) Tibia
j) Fibula
e) Tendon

Worksheet 5: Sport links and twitch muscle fibres, Levels A and B

1.

Fast twitch	Slow twitch
Contract fast, producing a powerful action; Tire quickly; Produce short bursts of energy; Suit sprinting and throwing events	Suited to slow, prolonged activity; Stay efficient over long periods; Have a very good oxygen supply; Best for events that take a long time to complete, such as long-distance running, swimming and cycling

2. (Level A only)
For slow twitch muscle fibres: any long-distance event
For fast twitch muscle fibres: any explosive, quick, powerful event

Homework 1: Functions of the muscles

a) extends the foot at the ankle
b) rotates at the shoulder
c) adducts at the arms/pulls arms back
d) extends at the hip

Homework 2: Muscles of the body

1.

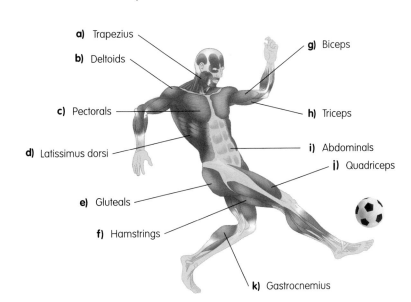

a) Trapezius
g) Biceps
b) Deltoids
c) Pectorals
h) Triceps
i) Abdominals
d) Latissimus dorsi
j) Quadriceps
e) Gluteals
f) Hamstrings
k) Gastrocnemius

2. a) Biceps/triceps

Hamstrings/quadriceps

    b) To flex at the elbow – biceps muscle pulls = prime mover contracts and shortens, the other triceps muscle relaxes = antagonist and lengthens.

To extend at the knee – quadriceps muscle pulls = prime mover contracts and shortens – hamstrings relax = antagonist and lengthens.

Homework 3: Multiple-choice questions

1. d   **2.** a   **3.** d   **4.** c

Extension 1: Posture

2. Answers should include:

Good posture:

- Shoulders and back should be straight and in line with the rest of the body.
- Head and chin should be up, in line with the body.
- Hips should be in line with the spine and feet.
- Spine should be as straight as possible.

Bad posture:

- Shoulders are rounded and not in line with the body.
- Head is positioned forward, straining the neck muscles.
- Hips are sagging, putting pressure on the spine.
- Spine is curved, creating a slouched look.

Extension 2: Fast and slow muscle twitch fibres

1. Fast twitch muscle fibres

1. Not as good supply of oxygen as STMF
2. Contractions are fast
3. Fast, powerful action
4. Tire quickly
5. Used for speed/explosive events
6. White in colour

Slow twitch muscle fibres

- Good oxygen supply
- Gets energy by using oxygen
- Contractions are slow
- Can work over prolonged periods
- Can repeat many times
- Used for endurance events
- Dark red in colour
- Use myglobin/mitochondria

2. Answers could include:

- Muscles have both types, but the amounts may differ.
- Nervous system only activates STMF when jogging/slow cycling, and so on.
- When explosive actions are needed both STMF and FTMF are used.
- Athletes are fibre tested.
- Long-distance eventers = STMF
- Sprinters/jumper/throwers = FTMF
- Although you cannot change genetic allocation you can train to improve each type efficiency.

Extension 3: Questions requiring short answers

a) pull

b) shorter

c) tendons

d) the origin

e) the insertion

f) antagonistic

g) prime mover

h) antagonist

i) sprinting, javelin, shot-put, high jump

j) any long-distance events like cycling, swimming and running

k) Bursts of energy; explosive events; tires quickly; contract fast; white in colour; only a fairly good oxygen supply

l) Used in prolonged activities; suited to long-distance events; able to work for a long time; contracts slowly; red in colour; very good oxygen supply

m) A state of the muscles' readiness to work

n) Giving space for the following to work properly: heart beat, digestive system, breathing, bone alignment; helping muscles keep their energy; personal self-esteem

1.2.5 A healthy, active lifestyle and your skeletal system

Bones
Worksheet 1: Protecting bones, Levels A and B

1. • Cranium: brain
   • Ribs: heart, lungs, liver, spleen
   • Pelvic girdle: female reproductive organs, bladder
   • Vertebral column: spinal chord

Worksheet 2: Functions of the skeleton, Levels A and B

a) shape   **b)** support   **c)** movements   **d)** protected   **e)** produced

Worksheet 3: Grouping and classifying bones, Levels A and B

Long bones – Tibia, fibula, humerus, ulna, femur, radius
Short bones – Phalanges, metatarsals, tarsals, metacarpals, carpals
Irregular bones – Thoracic vertebrae, sacral vertebrae, coccyx, patella, atlas, lumbar vertebrae, axis, cervical vertebrae
Flat bones – Cranium, ribs, sternum, clavicle, scapula

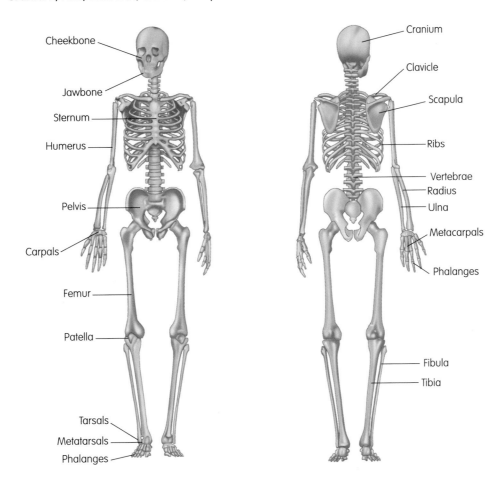

Worksheet 4: Bones that link with sporting actions, Levels A and B

Possible answers include:
a) scapula, humerus, ulna, radius, carpals, metacarpals, phalanges
b) scapula, humerus, ulna, radius, carpals, metacarpals, phalanges
c) pelvis, femur, patella, tibia, fibia, tarsals, metatarsals, phalanges
d) humerus, ulna, radius

Homework 1: Naming bones

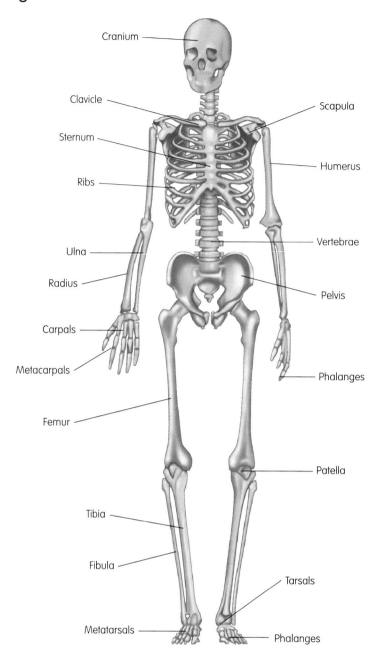

Cranium

Clavicle

Sternum

Ribs

Ulna

Radius

Carpals

Metacarpals

Femur

Tibia

Fibula

Metatarsals

Scapula

Humerus

Vertebrae

Pelvis

Phalanges

Patella

Tarsals

Phalanges

Homework 2: Interpreting information

a) 33

b) Thoracic

c) Lumbar

d) Help with breathing and protect spinal chord

e) Sacral and coccyx

Homework 3: Multiple-choice questions

1. c   **2.** b   **3.** a   **4.** c

Extension 1: Bones that protect

1. • Cranium – brain
   • Ribs – vital organs in the chest area: heart, liver, spleen, lungs
   • Pelvic girdle – bladder, female reproductive organs
   • Vertebral column – spinal chord

Extension 2: Bones and sport

Possible answers include:

Type of bone	Name of bone	Sporting action
Long bone	Radius	Rebounds the ball when playing a volleyball dig
Short bone	Carpals	Help spin the ball in cricket
Flat bone	Sternum	Rebound the ball when chesting down a ball in football

Extension 3: Questions on bones

a) Shape – gives shape and framework of the body, giving a person their particular build
   Support – gives a rigid framework for parts of the body to hang from and provides the muscles with an anchor to attach
   Movement aid – working with muscles, the different bones of the skeleton allow a variety of movements
   Protection – certain bones form a cage or box to protect the vital organs of the body
   Production of red blood cells – the cells are being used all the time, so a constant production is necessary for the transportation of oxygen to the working parts of the body

b) Possible answer includes: Vertebrae – protect spinal chord. Important in contact sports such as rugby, where impact with other players is common.

c) They are in a position where there is a great deal of movement, therefore they need to be robust to cope with the weight, stress and movement at this area.

d) Scapula, humerus, ulna, radius, carpals, metacarpals and phalanges

e) The shape of the person may suit a particular sport, for example, long – basketball player, short and thin – jockey

Joints

Worksheet 5: Names and locations of synovial joints, Levels A and B

Location	Neck	Knee	Hip	Elbow	Shoulder
Type of joint	pivot	hinge	ball and socket	hinge	ball and socket
Bones involved	atlas/axis	femur/tibia	pelvis/femur	humerus/ulna	scapula/humerus

Worksheet 6: Types of synovial joint, Levels A and B

a) Hinge joint – femur, tibia, patella
b) Ball and socket joint – scapula, humerus
c) Pivot joint – atlas, axis

Worksheet 7: Types of movement at a joint, Levels A and B

1. **a)** 1   **b)** 2   **c)** 4   **d)** 5   **e)** 3

3. **a)** ball and socket   **b)** ball and socket   **c)** hinge
   d) hinge   **e)** pivot

Worksheet 8: Action/movement/joint, Levels A and B

Example	Area	Type of joint	Type of movement	Description of the action
Kicking a football	Knee	Hinge	Extension	Lower leg moves forward to straighten after contact with the ball.
Hurdler lifting lead leg to clear a hurdle	Pelvis	Ball and socket	Rotation	Trailing leg clears close to hurdle and lands on the ground in front.
Swimmer performing front crawl arm action	Shoulder	Ball and socket	Rotation	Shoulder circles to allow the arm to reach forward to pull against the water.
Shooting arm action when scoring in basketball or netball	Elbow	Hinge	Extension	From a flexed position the triceps pull so the arm extends to pass the ball forward.

Worksheet 9: Linking muscles to sport, Levels A and B

Possible answers include:

Muscle name	Type of movement	Sport example	Description of action
Biceps	Flexion	Basketball	Flexion of elbow as player prepares to shoot
Triceps	Extension	Badminton	As angle increases at elbow as racket is in 'throwing' action of an overhead clear
Deltoids	Rotation	Golf	Of shoulder during golf swing
Pectorals	Abduction	Swimming – breast-stroke	During pull phase of breast-stroke arm action
Trapezius	Abduction	Swimming – butterfly	Elevation of arms and shoulders during butterfly arm action
Latissimus dorsi	Adduction	Rowing	Bring arms in during pull phase when rowing
Abdominals	Flexion	Pole vault	As angle decreases at hip as legs brought upward in pole vault
Gluteals	Extension	Weightlifting	As angle at hip increases weightlifter comes to a standing position
Quadriceps	Extension	Sprinting	As angle increases at knee during a kick in football
Hamstring	Flexion	Sprinting	As angle decreases at knee and prepares to stride forward during sprinting
Gastrocnemius	Extension	Athletics – long jump	As angle of ankle decreases during take-off

Homework 4: Description of movement at a joint

1. a) Ball and socket joint   **b)** Hinge joint   **c)** Pivot joint

Homework 5: Multiple-choice questions on joints

1. b   **2.** c   **3.** a   **4.** c

Homework 6: Common injuries

soft tissue injuries; muscles; joints; ligaments; stretching; Striding; turning; rest; compression; actions; order of treatment; damage; reduces the swelling; Compressing; throbbing; tendons; sport too much; incorrectly sized

Homework 7: Major injuries

Injury	How it happens	When it happens	Where it happens	How to avoid it
Torn cartilage	By excessive twisting of the joint.	When a player changes direction at speed.	Common in footballers.	Difficult to avoid – possibly make sure knee is as strong as possible.
Dislocation	The joint is moved outside its designed range.	After a forceful blow of the joint.	All major joints are vulnerable.	Strength training for muscles and tissues around the joint.
Fracture	If excessive impact or force is put on the bone.	After a blow or twist of the bone.	Depends on the activity. Football – leg/femur. Rugby – clavicle.	Difficult to avoid in contact sports.

Homework 8: Torn cartilage, dislocation and fractures

Dislocation: **a)** 5 **b)** 4 **c)** 1 **d)** 6 **e)** 3 **f)** 7 **g)** 2
Fractures: **a)** 7 **b)** 3 **c)** 4 **d)** 2 **e)** 6 **f)** 5 **g)** 1
Torn cartilage: **a)** 5 **b)** 6 **c)** 3 **d)** 2 **e)** 1 **f)** 4

Extension 4: Synovial joints and the sportsperson

1. Possible answers include:
- Cartilage stops friction of the bones and acts as a shock absorber, essential when running.
- Synovial fluid lubricates the joint, making movement in joint smooth.
- Ligaments join bone to bone and keep the joint together so changing of direction under pressure can occur without injury.
- Tendons join muscle to bone, allowing movement to take place.

2. Mark answers on own merits.

Extension 5: Types of movement and sports actions

1. Possible answers include:
1. Flexion
2. Extension
3. Abduction
4. Adduction
5. Rotation

2. Possible answers include: Chest passing – extension – angle increases between joints to make the pass – fingers/hinge, elbows/hinge and shoulders/ball and socket.
Hook shot – rotation – shoulder rolls overhead to make the shot – shoulder/ball and socket.

Extension 6: Questions requiring short answers

1. a) Synovial joints **b)** Hinge joint **c)** Hip **d)** Attach bone to bone
e) Abduction **f)** Flexion **g)** Rotation **h)** When older

Student's Book answers

1.1.1 Healthy, active lifestyles and how they could benefit you

Task 2

a) Mental   **b)** Physical   **c)** Social   **d)** Physical   **e)** Mental   **f)** Social

Exam questions

1. a) C   **b)** D   **c)** D   **d)** C

2. Physical activity

3. i) Physical   **ii)** Mental   **iii)** Social

4. Possible answers include:
- Burning up stored fat
- Look good/feel good
- Improve body image
- Increase muscle tone – posture improvement
- Bone strengthening
- Improves flexibility – more efficient movement
- Cardiovascular improvement – less prone to disease
- Less prone to injury
- Can increase life expectancy

5. Possible answers include:
- Meet people
- Mix with like-minded people
- Go with current friends
- Feel good about themselves
- Competition
- Improve performance
- For the challenge
- Keep cardiovascular systems working well
- Help to manage arthritis

1.1.2a Influences on your healthy, active lifestyle: key influences that impact on achieving sustained involvement in physical activity

Task 2

Possible answers include:
- Has put training first, trains regularly and at the right level. This shows determination and commitment which are good qualities to be linked with.
- Has achieved Olympic success and is at the top level in her field.
- Has achieved at an international level.
- Having competed on behalf of Great Britain, the whole nation can be proud of her success.
- Is a determined, hard worker and is good under pressure.
  All of these qualities would be good for a company/product to be associated with.

Task 10

a) Table tennis   **b)** Golf   **c)** Golf   **d)** Group 4

Exam questions

1. a) B   **b)** A   **c)** C   **2.** C

3. Any two from age, disability, gender, race and socio-economic status

4. Mark on own merits

5. Pay-per-view

6.
- Resources – availability, access, location, time
- People – family, peers, role models
- Image of activity – media coverage, fashion
- Cultural influences – race, gender, disability, age
- Socio-economic – status, cost
- Health and well-being

7.
- Access to facilities; stair lifts, changing areas, toilets
- Adapted equipment available for use
- Integration with able-bodied participants
- Availability of specialist coaching

1.1.2b Influences on your healthy, active lifestyle: opportunities, pathways and initiatives for involvement in physical activity

Exam questions

1. a) A **b)** C **2. a)** B **3.** D **4.** TOP Programme

5. Advises them on where, what to provide and how to maintain it.

6. Answers to include:
- Start – increase participation in physical activity and so improve health of the nation.
- Stay – create a network of clubs/coaches/sports facilities/volunteers so people have the chance to remain involved in sport.
- Succeed – create opportunities for talented athletes to succeed.

7. Answers to include:
- Centres of Excellence all over the country.
- Top coaches attracted.
- Facilities open to the public.

1.1.3 Exercise and fitness as part of your healthy, active lifestyle

Task 3
Possible answers include:
- Cardiovascular – link the length of the event/match/extra time keeping oxygen to working muscles so they can still function – coordination/reaction time.
- Muscular strength – using body weight as resistance/power/balance – strength of muscles keeping body balanced.
- Muscular endurance – muscles cannot function if not trained – lack of oxygen present/lactic acid build up/link with length of event – if trained keep working over long periods – coordination/reaction time/power/speed.
- Flexibility – joints able to move to full range – player can stretch for the ball/assume difficult positions – able to keep agile and balanced.
- Body composition – can affect the range of movement available so affects agility.

Exam questions

1. a) D **b)** B **2. a)** B **b)** B

3. Any long-distance event – canoeing/running/cycling – Tour de France **4.** Power

5. Mark on own merits

6. Strength = apply force and overcome resistance or ability to lift a maximum weight in one attempt.
   Endurance = muscles work for long periods without tiring.
- Body composition: shooter needs to be the right shape to play basketball: enough weight to resist the opposition, enough muscle for strength and power, but not so defined that flexibility is restricted.

1.1.4a Physical activity as part of your healthy, active lifestyle: training principles and goal setting

Exam questions

1. a) C   **b)** B   **c)** D   **d)** B   **e)** C   **2.** Reversibility

3. 60–80 per cent of maximum heart rate

4. Increasing the intensity of the exercise gradually. As the body adapts to the training, staged increases in frequency, intensity and time are made. Making muscles work harder than normal. Increasing exercise above 60 per cent of maximum heart rate. Increasing oxygen uptake to supply muscles with oxygen.

1.1.4b Physical activity as part of your healthy, active lifestyle: assessing fitness and developing an exercise programme

Exam questions

1. a) B   **b)** A   **c)** C   **d)** A   **e)** D

2. D   **3.** B   **4. a)** A   **b)** C   **5.** B

6. D   **7.** 72 bpm   **8.** Anaerobic   **9.** Cardiovascular endurance

10. The Sit and Reach Flexibility Test

11. Answers to include:
- After a warm-up
- Long interval training
- Periods of 15 minutes: three minutes of activity, followed by resting times matching the active periods.

12. Answers to include:
- Variety – for interest
- Adaptable – work on own or in a group
- Prevents overuse injury
- Can be made to suit the individual
- Need to develop general fitness

13. Illinois Agility Run Test because it tests speed and the ability to change direction, necessary skills for avoiding the opposition when attacking or defending.

1.1.5 Your personal health and well-being

Exam questions

1. a) B   **b)** C   **c)** A   **d)** A   **e)** C   **f)** A

2. Carbohydrates

3. Answers can include:
- Provides energy
- Helps our bodies grow
- Contributes to good general health.
- Repairs injured tissue

4. Proteins, carbohydrates, fats, minerals, fibre

5. Answers can include:
a) Carbohydrate loading
b) Week before the event
- Day of the event
- During the event
- After the event

1.2.1a Physical activity and your healthy mind and body: your body and its effects on participation and performance

Task 3

Voluntary: controlled, consciously, most common
Involuntary: automatic, intestines, blood vessels, smooth
Cardiac: automatic, involuntary, heart, never rests

Task 4

1. **a)** Mesomorphic **b)** Mesomorphic **c)** Endomorphic **d)** Mesomorphic
   e) Mesomorphic **f)** Ectomorphic **g)** Endomorphic

2. Ectomorphic – small bones/lean/fragile/delicate body/narrow at hips and shoulders
   Mesomorphic – lots of muscle/large trunk/heavy chest/broad shoulders/narrow hips
   Endomorphic – tendency to put on fat/soft round shape/short tapered limbs/wide at hips.

Exam questions

1. B **2.** D **3.** B **4.** D **5.** Overweight

6. Possible answers include:
   - Too much calorie intake combined with little exercise equals weight gain.
   - Little calorie intake combined with more exercise equals weight loss.

7. Answers can include:
   - Diabetes
   - Heart disease
   - Early mortality
   - High blood pressure
   - Osteoarthritis

8. • Women have irregular periods.
   - Some suffer osteoporosis in later life.
   - Low food intake leads to malnutrition and greater risk of injuries.
   - Insufficient vitamins and minerals taken in to maintain a healthy body.
   - Loss of bone mass leading to injury.
   - Lack of eating leads to an energy drain affecting performance.

9. Bouts of depression, severe medical problems such as kidney damage, liver damage, possible death.

10. Possible answers include:
    - to suit a certain sport
    - affect how skills are performed.
    - affect necessary speed over distance
    - speed of skill execution
    - affect fatigue
    - affect strength
    - variations may change success rate
    - affects suitability for a position in a team
    - flexibility may be hindered

1.2.1b Physical activity and your healthy mind and body: substances and the sportsperson

Task 3

- Litter – cuts/falls/abrasions
- Personal presentation – laces/fingernails/jewellery/no shin pads
- Balanced competition – big boy versus small boy
- Mix of sports – striking game hitting into different area
- Condition of the area – fence/posts/surface unsuitable for netball/divots to trip on

- Spectators – too close causing trips/falls/intimidating
- Dog – causing trips/falls

Task 6

A = rugby boots – rugby – are suitable for playing on soft ground and are flexible to allow running movement

B = gym slippers – gymnastics – these are light, provide maximum movement and give toes protection

C = spikes – sprinting – provide maximum movement of the foot and gives grip on the ground to improve speed

D = climbing shoe – mountain climbing – give maximum flexibility of the foot, gives ankle protection and the rubber sole grips the rock

Task 8

1. f	**2.** c	**3.** b	**4.** h	**5.** j
6. e	**7.** a	**8.** i	**9.** g	**10.** d

Exam questions

1. a) A	**b)** D	**c)** C	**2.** C	**3.** D
4. C	**5.** B	**6.** D		

7. a) Reduced feeling of tiredness, more alert, able to train for longer.
   b) Athletes relying on reactions.

8. To steady their hand, to keep calm.

9. Answers could include:
- Grading – reaching a particular standard and competing against those in the same category.
- Skill level – being skilful enough to play in a certain team irrespective of age.
- Weight – can be an advantage so particular categories are formed for fairness.
- Age – with age comes maturity and personal development; some sports have sophisticated strategies; by grouping young people in ages can make for fairer competition.
- Gender – younger children of both sexes can compete against each other. When boys develop physically, same sex competition can become dangerous.

10. Keep order/safe/fair/flow of the game/discipline/foul play.

11. a) High proportion of muscle, bone, large trunk, heavy chest, broad shoulders and narrow hips.
   b) Team game/gymnast, and so on.

12. Possible answers include:
Liver damage, dehydration, sedative, slows reactions, impairs judgement, loss of motor skills, aerobic capacity reduced, less energy, heat loss, longer recovery time from injury, masks pain, greater risk of muscle cramps

1.2.2 A healthy, active lifestyle and your cardiovascular system

Task 5

a) erythrocytes
b) carry oxygen
c) transportation of oxygen
d) fighting infection at the source, repairing tissue and destroying bacteria
e) leukocytes
f) the marrow of long bones and the lymph tissue of the body
g) to clot blood
h) larger cells
i) 55 per cent of the volume of blood
j) blood flow easier

Task 6

1. Keep to optimum body weight; don't smoke; avoid drinking alcohol excessively; eat less salt; avoid stress; exercise regularly
2. The wrist, neck or groin
3. Because they are pumped directly from the heart
4. Systolic
5. Valves closing
6. 120 over 180
7. Exercise, sleep, age and gender

Exam questions

1. a) B   b) C   c) A   d) D

2. Cardiac output   3. Red blood cells

4. Answers can include:

Heart rate increases; stroke volume increases; cardiac output increases; blood is shunted to the working muscles; systems such as the digestive system are by-passed by the blood; oxygen and haemoglobin combine (oxyhaemoglobin) and are transported to working muscles; amount of exercise influences the heart rate; cardiac centre controls and regulates the heart rate; blood vessels dilate at skin surface, to release heat, causing skin to redden; waste products such as salt and water exit body via pores and capillaries at skin surface; the endothelium of the arteries automatically widens to let more blood through.

5. Answers can include:
- Heart strengthens
- Heart rate returns to resting rate quicker
- Heart increases in size
- Resting stroke volume increases
- Cardiac output increases
- Resting heart rate decreases

6. Answers can include:
- Stronger heart – lasts longer
- Lower resting rate – transports sufficient blood with less beats
- Lower active heart rate – less stress on heart
- Increased VO_2 max
- Can cope with increased stress more effectively
- Can deliver oxygen to the working muscles more effectively
- Recover from the stress of exercise quicker
- Reduce risks of heart disease
- Reduced risk of coronary artery disease

1.2.3 A healthy, active lifestyle and your respiratory system

Task 4

f), b), e), d), a), c), f)

Exam questions

1. a) D   b) C   c) A

2. Inhaled – trace
   Exhaled 4%

3. The alveoli

4. Glucose ⟶ energy + lactic acid

5. a) Aerobic   b) Anaerobic   c) Both aerobic and anaerobic

6. a) Body converts fuel into energy in the presence of oxygen
   b) Any long-distance athlete
   c) glucose + oxygen = carbon dioxide + water + energy

7. Composition of inhaled air
   79% = nitrogen
   20% = oxygen
   trace = carbon dioxide

   Composition of exhaled air
   79% = nitrogen
   16% = oxygen
   4% = carbon dioxide

8. Answers can include:
- Oxygen inhaled regularly for aerobic respiration; tidal volume increases.
- Air exhaled to stop the build-up of carbon dioxide.
- Breathing rate increases and becomes deeper and more regular = aerobic respiration.
- After short bursts of all-out effort breathing is shallow and gasping, attempting to repay the oxygen debt (anaerobic).
- Gaseous exchange in alveoli – with training the gaseous exchange becomes more efficient as more alveoli are prepared to take on the exchange of oxygen and carbon dioxide.
- Waste water released from the body as sweat on surface of the skin.
- Release of energy – glycogen is stored in muscles and the liver and is released as glucose to allow the muscles to work.

9. Breathing becomes shallow resulting in gasping for breath – a result of oxygen debt

10. The ability to breathe in more air for longer; a greater amount of oxygen enters the body for use by muscles; the quality of blood increases – more red cells means a greater chance of oxyhaemoglobin being delivered to working muscles.

1.2.4 A healthy, active lifestyle and your muscular system

Task 9

1. They increase in size, strength and tone

2. They increase in strength and tone

Exam questions

1. a) D
b) A
c) C

2. A
3. B
4. Isometric
5. Slow twitch muscle fibres

6. Muscles gain size and strength; muscles gain the ability to work for longer without tiring; muscles hypertrophy; muscles surrounding joint make it more stable.

7. Answers can include:
Result of overstretching; muscle is twisted and/or wrenched; poor warm-up; weakens the muscle.

1.2.5 A healthy, active lifestyle and your skeletal system

Task 9

Cartilage: hyaline, reduces friction, acts as a cushion, barrier between the bones
Synovial fluid: helps move freely, lubricates
Ligaments: elastic, stabilize, tough, attach bone to bone
Synovial capsule: tough fibre, surrounds the joint

Task 13

Size, produced, movements, anchor/frame, protected

Exam questions

1. a) C
b) C
c) D
d) A
e) D

2. Helps movement, protects, production of red blood cells
3. Rotation

4. a) Ball and socket at the shoulders
b) Fullest range – rotation and movements in different directions
c) Bones – scapula/humerus; synovial joint – cartilage/tendons/ligaments/synovial capsule/synovial membrane/synovial fluid

5. a) Stress fracture
b) Unusual, constant, repeated stress on the bone. Cracks occur in the bone
c) Rest – four to eight weeks. With gradual return to training with first two weeks being low impact.